RED READER

THE Tempest

WILLIAM SHAKESPEARE

Introduction, Synopses, and Annotations by Melanie Martin Long
Edited by Kara L. Quinn

TEACHER'S
Discovery™
©2003 American Eagle Co.

ISBN: 0-7560-0198-6

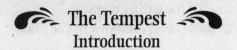

The Tempest
Introduction

If you want magic, mayhem, and adventure—not to mention romance and revenge—you've opened the right book. *The Tempest* has it all: a plotting sorcerer, a murderous man-monster, cunning traitors, spirits, lovers, all shipwrecked on an enchanted (and sometimes dangerous!) desert island. There's lots of double meaning if you're willing to look for it, underneath a funny, exciting story about a terrible storm and a man with a master plan: stuff about isolation, control, dreams, vengeance, and redemption. There are also some of Shakespeare's most famous lines (like "misery acquaints a man with strange bedfellows") and many of his most memorable characters, like master magician Prospero and the half-man, half-fish Caliban.

Speaking of Shakespeare, the guy was a memorable character himself. Rumor has it that this son of a glove-maker in Stratford-upon-Avon was first a schoolteacher—so look out—the next Shakespeare could be writing verb conjugations on your classroom chalkboard! He later moved to London where he was an actor and playwright for the Lord Chamberlain's Men. The guy was busy: he wrote lots of plays on his own (some were lost but we still have thirty-six of them) and a few more with his friends. And he wrote tons of poems, mostly sonnets. *The Tempest* was one of his last plays, written around 1611, just when people began settling the New World. So there are a number of (not entirely accurate) references to colonizing and native peoples. Lots of the characters in *The Tempest* are from Italy, but remember, Shakespeare lived in England and he didn't do much traveling, so these are Italians seen through British eyes.

People have been reading, performing, filming, adapting, and arguing about Shakespeare's plays for four hundred years. Not bad for a guy with a grammar school education who died when he was fifty-two. Why the endurance? Shakespeare wasn't just a great poet; he had his finger on a lot of the ideas and questions that make human beings tick. Like the way ambition can corrupt people (*Macbeth*, *Julius Caesar*), or the futility and destruction of a family feud (*Romeo and Juliet*) or—drum roll, please—our desire for revenge on those who wrong us and our capacity to forgive. And so we have *The Tempest*.

Enough for now about all this deep stuff—you'll get enough of it in the play if you feel like digging for it. If you don't, you can always fall back on the magic, mayhem, romance, and revenge! The cool thing about *The Tempest* is that it has both light and dark, both comedy and drama—and people like us at their best and worst.

So go for it! You'll be glad you did.

Dramatis Personae
(The dudes and dudettes in the play)

ISLAND PEOPLE

> **PROSPERO** - a magician with a mission and the rightful Duke of Milan

> **MIRANDA** - 15 years old, Prospero's daughter and Ferdinand's true love, the poster child for a sheltered upbringing

> **CALIBAN** - a half-man, half-monster with a grudge against father-figure Prospero

> **ARIEL** - Prospero's number-one, always-on-top-of-it spirit

Guest appearances by GODDESSES, NYMPHS, and SPIRITS, including:

> > **JUNO** - proud-as-a-peacock queen of gods

> > **CERES** - goddess of agriculture and fertility

> > **IRIS** - rainbow-lady messenger of the gods

SHIPWRECKED VISITORS

First, the royal court. . .

> **KING ALONSO** - King of Naples and grieving dad, a fish out of water on Prospero's island

> **FERDINAND** - King Alonso's son and Miranda's main squeeze

> **SEBASTIAN** - King Alonso's striving and conniving brother

> **ANTONIO** - Prospero's brother, the fake Duke of Milan, and the king of double-crossing

> **GONZALO** - an aging councilor to King Alonso, the Energizer Bunny of optimism

> **ADRIAN** - a young Gonzalo-in-training, a lord in the court

> **FRANCISCO** - also a young lord with only two lines in the play—see if you can find them

And now the rest of the gang. . .

> **TRINCULO** - a jester with a taste for wine and run-ins with strange bedfellows

> **STEPHANO** - a besotted butler with visions of grandeur and the brains of a buffoon

> **MASTER OF SHIP**- the captain of King Alonso's ill-fated voyage

> **BOATSWAIN** - a stellar first mate who tells it like it is

The Tempest
Act I, Scene I

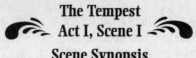

Scene Synopsis

The Boatswain and his crew try to fight a killer of a storm while King Alonso and all his royal pains in the butt—er, followers—wig out. The ship splinters, and the King, his followers, the Boatswain, and the crew are all flung to sea, presumably to drown.

Scene I

On a ship at sea: a tempestuous noise

On a ship at sea with thunder and lightning heard.

Enter a Master and a Boatswain

Pronounced "Bo-zen," the Boatswain is the first mate.

Master
> Boatswain!

Boatswain
> Here, master: what cheer?

what cheer = how are you

Master
> Good, speak to th' mariners: fall to't, yarely,
> or we run ourselves aground: bestir, bestir.

Sailing terms: Yarely or yare means briskly or actively.

Enter Mariners

Boatswain
> Heigh, my hearts! cheerly, cheerly, my hearts!
> yare, yare! Take in the topsail. Tend to th'
> master's whistle. Blow, till thou burst thy wind,
> if room enough!

In early sailing, a whistle was used to call sailors to their work.

Enter ALONSO, SEBASTIAN, ANTONIO, FERDINAND, GONZALO, and others

ALONSO
> Good boatswain, have care. Where's the master?
> Play the men.

Great. Just when the Bo-zen is trying to take care of things, the King and his entourage show up.

Boatswain
> I pray now, keep below.

ANTONIO
> Where is the master, bos'n?

Boatswain
> Do you not hear him? You mar our labor: keep your
> cabins: you do assist the storm.

Translation: Excuse me folks, but I'm, like, trying to save our LIVES here!

GONZALO
> Nay, good, be patient.

Boatswain
> When the sea is. Hence! What cares these roarers
> for the name of king? To cabin: silence! trouble us not.

Ever try to reason with a hurricane? Kings, laws, rich or poor—Mother Nature's an equal opportunity offender!

GONZALO
> Good, yet remember whom thou hast aboard.

Boatswain

None that I more love than myself. You are a
councilor; if you can command these elements to
silence, and work the peace of the present, we will
not hand a rope more; use your authority: if you
cannot, give thanks you have lived so long, and make
yourself ready in your cabin for the mischance of
the hour, if it so hap. Cheerly, good hearts! Out
of our way, I say.

Exeunt

GONZALO

I have great comfort from this fellow: methinks he
hath no drowning mark upon him; his complexion is
perfect gallows. Stand fast, good Fate, to his
hanging: make the rope of his destiny our cable,
for our own doth little advantage. If he be not
born to be hanged, our case is miserable.

Exit

Re-enter Boatswain

Boatswain

Down with the topmast! yare! lower, lower! Bring
her to try with main-course.

A cry within

A plague upon this howling! they are louder than
the weather or our office.

Re-enter SEBASTIAN, ANTONIO, and GONZALO

Yet again! what do you here? Shall we give o'er
and drown? Have you a mind to sink?

SEBASTIAN

A' pox o' your throat, you bawling, blasphemous,
incharitable dog!

Boatswain

Work you then.

ANTONIO

Hang, cur! hang, you whoreson, insolent noisemaker!
We are less afraid to be drowned than thou art.

GONZALO

I'll warrant him for drowning; though the ship were
no stronger than a nutshell and as leaky as an
unstanched wench.

Boatswain

Lay her ahold, ahold! set her two courses off to
sea again; lay her off.

Enter Mariners wet

Mariners

All lost! to prayers, to prayers! all lost!

Exeunt

2   ACT I   SCENE I

At least the Bo-zen is honest!

hand = handle

Exeunt = two or more (sometimes all) exit

Fate has chosen that our bud, the good Bo-zen, will die by hanging, NOT drowning. At least that's what Gonzalo hopes!

For Elizabethans, the Wheel of Fortune was more than just a game show.

The King and his gang are yelling louder than the storm.

Just when he gets rid of the King, his brother and the Duke of Milan show up!

Not the best time to go off on the Bo-zen, dudes. He's your last hope.

Insults won't get you anywhere.

Gonzalo is saying that the Bo-zen won't let them drown. Keep hoping, Gonzalo!

Lay her ahold = bring the ship near the wind
lay her off = take it to sea

Things are definitely not looking good.

Boatswain

What, must our mouths be cold?

GONZALO

The King and Prince at prayers! let's assist them,
For our case is as theirs.

SEBASTIAN

I'm out of patience.

What else is new, Sebastian?

ANTONIO

We are merely cheated of our lives by drunkards:
This wide-chopped rascal–would thou mightst lie drowning
The washing of ten tides!

Oh right. Like the storm is the Bo-zen's fault, Antonio. Blamer.

GONZALO

He'll be hanged yet,
Though every drop of water swear against it
And gape at wid'st to glut him.
    A confused noise within: 'Mercy on us!'– 'We split, we
split!'–'Farewell, my wife and children!'–
'Farewell, brother!'–'We split, we split, we split!'

St-i-i-i-ll hoping, Gonzalo!

Exit Boatswain

ANTONIO

Let's all sink with th' King.

SEBASTIAN

Let's take leave of him.

Exeunt ANTONIO and SEBASTIAN

GONZALO

Now would I give a thousand furlongs of sea for an
acre of barren ground, long heath, brown furze, anything. The wills above be done! but I would fain
die a dry death.

furlongs = eighths of a mile
heath = low-growing shrub
furze = gorse (a spiny shrub)
fain = rather

Exit

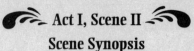

Act I, Scene II

Scene Synopsis

With a magician for a dad, Miranda knows who's really behind these weather patterns. She pleads with pop Prospero to stop the storm. Prospero assures her it's all a part of his master plan and tells her the story of how they got to the island. He checks in with his main spirit, Ariel, to make sure the dudes on board the ship (which included his double-crossing brother, Antonio, not to mention the King of Naples and his son Ferdinand) all came to the island alive. He disses Caliban, who's in the doghouse for trying to have his way with Miranda. When Ariel brings Prince Ferdinand to their island hang out, it's love at first sight for the prince and Miranda.

Scene II
The island. Before PROSPERO'S cell.

Enter PROSPERO and MIRANDA

MIRANDA

> If by your art, my dearest father, you have
> Put the wild waters in this roar, allay them.
> The sky, it seems, would pour down stinking pitch,
> But that the sea, mounting to th' welkin's cheek,
> Dashes the fire out. O, I have suffered
> With those that I saw suffer: a brave vessel,
> Who had, no doubt, some noble creature in her,
> Dashed all to pieces. O, the cry did knock
> Against my very heart. Poor souls, they perished.
> Had I been any god of power, I would
> Have sunk the sea within the earth or ere
> It should the good ship so have swallowed and
> The fraughting souls within her.

PROSPERO

> Be collected:
> No more amazement: tell your piteous heart
> There's no harm done.

MIRANDA

> O, woe the day!

PROSPERO

> No harm.
> I have done nothing but in care of thee,
> Of thee, my dear one, thee, my daughter, who
> Art ignorant of what thou art, naught knowing
> Of whence I am, nor that I am more better
> Than Prospero, master of a full poor cell,
> And thy no greater father.

MIRANDA

> More to know
> Did never meddle with my thoughts.

PROSPERO

> 'Tis time
> I should inform thee farther. Lend thy hand,
> And pluck my magic garment from me. So:

DOUBLE MEANING ALERT!!! (And we're only at the stage directions!) No man is an island, but Prospero is as close as you could get. He's isolated by geography and his outta-this-world magical powers. Maybe Shakespeare doesn't call his home a cell for nothing!

art = magic, power over nature

pitch = thick, dark, sticky stuff

Welkin's cheek means heaven's face.

Happy English Teacher Moment (H.E.T.): Onomatopoeia in "cry did knock." Good thing Miranda's not running things. She'd have dried the ocean before letting a ship wreck—imagine the changes to the ecosystem!

Notice Prospero and Miranda speak in verse. Shakespeare often used verse for high-born characters and prose for low-born ones, or clowns.

That's supposed to make her feel better?! You whipped up that storm for her?

Not the most curious of teenagers, is she?

Prospero wears a charmed garment—a mantle, or cloak.

Lays down his mantle

Lie there, my art. Wipe thou thine eyes; have comfort.
The direful spectacle of the wrack, which touched
The very virtue of compassion in thee,
I have with such provision in mine art
So safely ordered that there is no soul–
No, not so much perdition as an hair
Betid to any creature in the vessel
Which thou heard'st cry, which thou saw'st sink.
    Sit down;
For thou must now know farther.

MIRANDA
    You have often
Begun to tell me what I am, but stopped
And left me to a bootless inquisition,
Concluding 'Stay: not yet.'

PROSPERO
    The hour's now come;
The very minute bids thee ope thine ear;
Obey and be attentive. Canst thou remember
A time before we came unto this cell?
I do not think thou canst, for then thou wast not
Out three years old.

MIRANDA
    Certainly, sir, I can.

PROSPERO
    By what? by any other house or person?
Of any thing the image tell me that
Hath kept with thy remembrance.

MIRANDA
    'Tis far off
And rather like a dream than an assurance
That my remembrance warrants. Had I not
Four or five women once that tended me?

PROSPERO
    Thou hadst, and more, Miranda. But how is it
That this lives in thy mind? What seest thou else
In the dark backward and abysm of time?
If thou rememb'rest aught ere thou cam'st here,
How thou cam'st here thou mayst.

MIRANDA
    But that I do not.

PROSPERO
    Twelve year since, Miranda, twelve year since,
Thy father was the Duke of Milan and
A prince of power.

MIRANDA
    Sir, are not you my father?

PROSPERO

> Thy mother was a piece of virtue, and
> She said thou wast my daughter; and thy father
> Was Duke of Milan; and his only heir
> And princess no worse issued.

Third Clue: Prospero used to be a duke, Miranda, a princess. No wonder they could afford a babysitter brigade.

MIRANDA

> O the heavens!
> What foul play had we, that we came from thence?
> Or blessed was't we did?

PROSPERO

> Both, both, my girl:
> By foul play, as thou say'st, were we heaved thence,
> But blessedly holp hither.

Fourth Clue: They didn't leave Milan on a joy ride. Someone wanted them gone.

MIRANDA

> O, my heart bleeds
> To think o' th' teen that I have turned you to,
> Which is from my remembrance! Please you, farther.

teen = trouble, pain, anxiety
from = away from, not part of

PROSPERO

> My brother and thy uncle, called Antonio—
> I pray thee, mark me—that a brother should
> Be so perfidious!—he whom next thyself
> Of all the world I loved and to him put
> The manage of my state; as at that time
> Through all the signories it was the first
> And Prospero the prime duke, being so reputed
> In dignity, and for the liberal arts
> Without a parallel; those being all my study,
> The government I cast upon my brother
> And to my state grew stranger, being transported
> And rapt in secret studies. Thy false uncle—
> Dost thou attend me?

mark = listen
perfidious = treacherous

Signories were provinces of Italy.

Wait a sec. Big clues here. So Prospero let his brother, Antonio, govern Milan while he studied magic. OK, we're with you . . . .

MIRANDA

> Sir, most heedfully.

So is Miranda.

PROSPERO

> Being once perfected how to grant suits,
> How to deny them, who t' advance and who
> To trash for over-topping, new-created
> The creatures that were mine, I say, or changed 'em,
> Or else new formed 'em; having both the key
> Of officer and office, set all hearts i' th' state
> To what tune pleased his ear; that now he was
> The ivy which had hid my princely trunk,
> And sucked my verdure out on't. Thou attend'st not.

. . . and Antonio learned the ins and outs of politics and started putting ideas in peoples' heads; yeah, yeah, go on . . .

Prospero compares himself to a tree smothered by ivy.

MIRANDA

> O, good sir, I do.

We're ALL listening! Keep going!

PROSPERO

> I pray thee, mark me.
> I, thus neglecting worldly ends, all dedicated
> To closeness and the bettering of my mind

So while Prospero, like, ignored the day-to-day stuff of running Milan . . .

With that which, but by being so retired,
O'er-prized all popular rate, in my false brother
Awaked an evil nature; and my trust,
Like a good parent, did beget of him
A falsehood in its contrary as great
As my trust was; which had indeed no limit,
A confidence sans bound. He being thus lorded,
Not only with what my revenue yielded,
But what my power might else exact, like one
Who having into truth, by telling of it,
Made such a sinner of his memory,
To credit his own lie, he did believe
He was indeed the duke; out o' th' substitution
And executing th' outward face of royalty,
With all prerogative: hence his ambition growing—
Dost thou hear?

> . . . Antonio started to believe in a lie even bigger than the trust Prospero had put in him. OK, still with you . . .

> Will the real Duke of Milan please stand up? Sounds like Antonio moved in on Prospero's turf.

> Wait, you mean this gets worse?

MIRANDA
Your tale, sir, would cure deafness.

> We ALL hear! Keep going!

PROSPERO
To have no screen between this part he played
And him he played it for, he needs will be
Absolute Milan. Me, poor man, my library
Was dukedom large enough: of temporal royalties
He thinks me now incapable; confederates—
So dry he was for sway—with th' King of Naples
To give him annual tribute, do him homage,
Subject his coronet to his crown and bend
The dukedom yet unbow'd—alas, poor Milan!—
To most ignoble stooping.

> Absolute Milan means the bro wants the kingdom all to himself.

> So Antonio starts making payments to Alonso (a.k.a. King of Naples) for protection. What is this, the mafia?

MIRANDA
O the heavens!

PROSPERO
Mark his condition and th' event; then tell me
If this might be a brother.

> Prospero's Rule #1: Just when you think it couldn't get worse . . .

MIRANDA
I should sin
To think but nobly of my grandmother:
Good wombs have borne bad sons.

PROSPERO
Now the condition.
The King of Naples, being an enemy
To me inveterate, hearkens my brother's suit;
Which was, that he, in lieu o' th' premises
Of homage and I know not how much tribute,
Should presently extirpate me and mine
Out of the dukedom and confer fair Milan
With all the honors on my brother: whereon,
A treacherous army levied, one midnight
Fated to th' purpose did Antonio open
The gates of Milan, and, i' th' dead of darkness,

> . . . it gets worse.

> With the King of Naples, flattery will get you everywhere, even into your brother's dukedom.

> army levied = soldiers raised for war

The ministers for th' purpose hurried thence
Me and thy crying self.

MIRANDA

> Alack, for pity!
> not rememb'ring how I cried out then,
> Will cry it o'er again: it is a hint
> That wrings mine eyes to't.

PROSPERO

> Hear a little further
> And then I'll bring thee to the present business
> Which now's upon's; without the which this story
> Were most impertinent.

MIRANDA

> Wherefore did they not
> That hour destroy us?

PROSPERO

> Well demanded, wench:
> My tale provokes that question. Dear, they durst not,
> So dear the love my people bore me, nor set
> A mark so bloody on the business, but
> With colors fairer painted their foul ends.
> In few, they hurried us aboard a bark,
> Bore us some leagues to sea; where they prepared
> A rotten carcass of a butt, not rigged,
> Nor tackle, sail, nor mast; the very rats
> Instinctively have quit it: there they hoist us,
> To cry to th' sea that roared to us, to sigh
> To th' winds whose pity, sighing back again,
> Did us but loving wrong.

MIRANDA

> Alack, what trouble
> Was I then to you!

PROSPERO

> O, a cherubin
> Thou wast that did preserve me. Thou didst smile.
> Infused with a fortitude from heaven,
> When I have decked the sea with drops full salt,
> Under my burden groaned; which raised in me
> An undergoing stomach, to bear up
> Against what should ensue.

MIRANDA

> How came we ashore?

PROSPERO

> By providence divine.
> Some food we had and some fresh water that
> A noble Neapolitan, Gonzalo,
> Out of his charity, who being then appointed
> Master of this design, did give us, with
> Rich garments, linens, stuffs and necessaries,
> Which since have steaded much; so, of his gentleness,

Booted out of his kingdom. That's harsh. Whatever happened to brotherly love?

hint = occasion

Right, the present business. What's this family history got to do with the storm?

At least Prospero's ratings were good. Otherwise, he wouldn't be alive.

bark = boat

butt = tub, barrel
You know it's bad when the rats won't sail with you.

She wasn't trouble; she was an angel. "Thank heaven, for little girls!" Come on everybody, sing along!

undergoing stomach = guts, strength

Even then, Gonzalo was an optimist.

Knowing I loved my books, he furnished me
From mine own library with volumes that
I prize above my dukedom.

MIRANDA

      Would I might
But ever see that man!

PROSPERO

      Now I arise:

Resumes his mantle

Sit still, and hear the last of our sea-sorrow.
Here in this island we arrived; and here
Have I, thy schoolmaster, made thee more profit
Than other princesses can that have more time
For vainer hours and tutors not so careful.

MIRANDA

Heavens thank you for't! And now, I pray you, sir,
For still 'tis beating in my mind, your reason
For raising this sea-storm?

PROSPERO

      Know thus far forth.
By accident most strange, bountiful Fortune,
Now my dear lady, hath mine enemies
Brought to this shore; and by my prescience
I find my zenith doth depend upon
A most auspicious star, whose influence
If now I court not but omit, my fortunes
Will ever after droop. Here cease more questions:
Thou art inclined to sleep; 'tis a good dullness,
And give it way: I know thou canst not choose.

MIRANDA sleeps

Come away, servant, come. I am ready now.
Approach, my Ariel, come.

Enter ARIEL

ARIEL

All hail, great master! grave sir, hail! I come
To answer thy best pleasure; be't to fly,
To swim, to dive into the fire, to ride
On the curled clouds, to thy strong bidding task
Ariel and all his quality.

PROSPERO

      Hast thou, spirit,
Performed to point the tempest that I bade thee?

ARIEL

To every article.
I boarded the King's ship; now on the beak,
Now in the waist, the deck, in every cabin,
I flamed amazement: sometime I'd divide,
And burn in many places; on the topmast,
The yards and bowsprit, would I flame distinctly,

Guess there wasn't much point in getting Prospero's nose out of the magic books then—he'd already lost his dukedom.

Finally, we're going to find out about the tempest.

Okay!! So Miranda's had a lot of time to study! What about the storm?!

It's beating in our minds too, Prospero!

FINALLY we get it. Fate brought the ship into Prospero's "magic range." And look what the storm washed up: the same people who kicked Prospero out of Milan!

Prospero's Rule #2: When you don't feel like answering any more questions, put whoever's asking them to sleep.

Ariel is a spirit from the world of Prospero's Art.

Ariel's the hippest spirit on the island, but here "quality" means the other sprites he works with.

beak = prow of ship

waist = middle of ship

bowsprit = pole extending from prow

Then meet and join. Jove's lightnings, the precursors
O' th' dreadful thunderclaps, more momentary
And sight-outrunning were not; the fire and cracks
Of sulphurous roaring the most mighty Neptune
Seem to besiege and make his bold waves tremble,
Yea, his dread trident shake.

PROSPERO

My brave spirit!
Who was so firm, so constant, that this coil
Would not infect his reason?

ARIEL

Not a soul
But felt a fever of the mad and played
Some tricks of desperation. All but mariners
Plunged in the foaming brine and quit the vessel,
Then all afire with me: the King's son, Ferdinand,
With hair up-staring,—then like reeds, not hair,—
Was the first man that leapt; cried, 'Hell is empty
And all the devils are here.'

PROSPERO

Why that's my spirit!
But was not this nigh shore?

ARIEL

Close by, my master.

PROSPERO

But are they, Ariel, safe?

ARIEL

Not a hair perished;
On their sustaining garments not a blemish,
But fresher than before: and, as thou bad'st me,
In troops I have dispersed them 'bout the isle.
The King's son have I landed by himself;
Whom I left cooling of the air with sighs
In an odd angle of the isle and sitting,
His arms in this sad knot.

PROSPERO

Of the King's ship
The mariners say how thou hast disposed
And all the rest o' th' fleet.

ARIEL

Safely in harbor
Is the King's ship; in the deep nook, where once
Thou call'dst me up at midnight to fetch dew
From the still-vexed Bermoothes, there she's hid:
The mariners all under hatches stowed;
Who, with a charm joined to their suff'red labor,
I have left asleep; and for the rest o' th' fleet
Which I dispersed, they all have met again
And are upon the Mediterranean flote,
Bound sadly home for Naples,

Translation: I was quicker than lightning (another inverted sentence).

Mythology Check! Neptune, sea-god

Who knew Ariel moonlighted as special effects guy on *The Perfect Storm*?

Give the man details, Ariel! Which of them was the biggest wimp?

brine = saltwater

And the prize goes to . . . Ferdinand!

Notice how Prospero and Ariel's short lines can be joined together to make one long line, These "shared lines" are Shakespeare's cue to actors to keep up the pace of the conversation. They happen throughout *The Tempest*.

Safe, nearby, clothes like new, divided into the right groups— this spirit knows how to follow directions!

Called up at midnight to work? Sounds like Prospero's a slave driver!

Bermoothes = The Bermudas; considered a place of tempests and enchantments (Where do you think "Bermuda Triangle" comes from?)

flote = ocean

Supposing that they saw the King's ship wracked
And his great person perish.

PROSPERO

      Ariel, thy charge
Exactly is performed: but there's more work.
What is the time o' th' day?

ARIEL

      Past the mid season.

mid season = midday

PROSPERO

      At least two glasses. The time 'twixt six and now
Must by us both be spent most preciously.

glasses, as in hourglasses

ARIEL

      Is there more toil? Since thou dost give me pains,
Let me remember thee what thou hast promised,
Which is not yet performed me.

PROSPERO

      How now? moody?
What is't thou canst demand?

ARIEL

      My liberty.

So . . . the shipwreck wasn't
just a favor among friends—
Prospero really *is* a slave driver.

PROSPERO

      Before the time be out? no more!

ARIEL

      I prithee,
Remember I have done thee worthy service;
Told thee no lies, made thee no mistakings, served
Without or grudge or grumblings: thou didst promise
To bate me a full year.

prithee = a squished together
"pray thee"; i.e., "I beg you" or
"please"

bate me = let me off

PROSPERO

      Dost thou forget
From what a torment I did free thee?

Prospero's Rule #2: When your
fairies give you attitude, show
'em who's boss!

ARIEL

      No.

PROSPERO

      Thou dost, and think'st it much to tread the ooze
Of the salt deep,
To run upon the sharp wind of the North,
To do me business in the veins o' th' earth
When it is baked with frost.

baked = hardened

ARIEL

      I do not, sir.

PROSPERO

      Thou liest, malignant thing! Hast thou forgot
The foul witch Sycorax, who with age and envy
Was grown into a hoop? hast thou forgot her?

First Prospero, now Ariel—
everybody on this island has got
a story!

grown into a hoop = stooped
over

ARIEL

      No, sir.

PROSPERO

    Thou hast. Where was she born? speak; tell me.

ARIEL

    Sir, in Argier.

                                                          Argier is the old name for Algiers.

PROSPERO

    O, was she so? I must
Once in a month recount what thou hast been,
Which thou forget'st. This damned witch Sycorax,
For mischiefs manifold and sorceries terrible
To enter human hearing, from Argier,
Thou know'st, was banished: for one thing she did
They would not take her life. Is not this true?

                                                          OK, so this witch Sycorax was banished to this island. What's that got to do with Ariel?

ARIEL

    Ay, sir.

PROSPERO

    This blue-eyed hag was hither brought with child
And here was left by th' sailors. Thou, my slave,
As thou report'st thyself, wast then her servant;
And, for thou wast a spirit too delicate
To act her earthy and abhorred commands,
Refusing her grand hests, she did confine thee,
By help of her more potent ministers
And in her most unmitigable rage,
Into a cloven pine; within which rift
Imprisoned thou didst painfully remain
A dozen years; within which space she died
And left thee there; where thou didst vent thy groans
As fast as millwheels strike. Then was this island–
Save for the son that she did litter here,
A freckled whelp hag-born–not honored with
A human shape.

                                                           Blue eyelids were thought to be a sign of pregnancy.

                                                          Ohhh—so she was Ariel's ex-boss!

                                                           hests = demands

                                                          unmitigable = unappeasable, unstoppable

                                                          Twelve years trapped inside a tree for disobeying your boss? Ariel, dude, that's harsh!

                                                          Wait. This witch had a kid?

ARIEL

    Yes, Caliban her son.

PROSPERO

    Dull thing, I say so; he, that Caliban
Whom now I keep in service. Thou best know'st
What torment I did find thee in; thy groans
Did make wolves howl and penetrate the breasts
Of ever-angry bears: it was a torment
To lay upon the damned, which Sycorax
Could not again undo: it was mine art,
When I arrived and heard thee, that made gape
The pine and let thee out.

                                                          And now he works for Prospero.

                                                          No wonder Ariel fears Prospero—his magic was the only thing able to set Ariel free from the tree . . .

ARIEL

    I thank thee, master.

PROSPERO

    If thou more murmur'st, I will rend an oak
And peg thee in his knotty entrails till
Thou hast howled away twelve winters.

                                                          . . . And can put him back again. Yikes!

ARIEL

    Pardon, master;
I will be correspondent to command
And do my spiriting gently.

PROSPERO

    Do so, and after two days
I will discharge thee.

ARIEL

    That's my noble master!
What shall I do? say what; what shall I do?

PROSPERO

    Go make thyself like a nymph o' th' sea: be subject
To no sight but thine and mine, invisible
To every eyeball else. Go take this shape
And hither come in't: go, hence with diligence!

Exit ARIEL

    Awake, dear heart, awake! thou hast slept well; Awake!

Slave driver one minute, loving dad the next—what's Prospero's deal?

MIRANDA

The strangeness of your story put
Heaviness in me.

PROSPERO

    Shake it off. Come on;
We'll visit Caliban my slave, who never
Yields us kind answer.

MIRANDA

    'Tis a villain, sir,
I do not love to look on.

PROSPERO

    But, as 'tis,
We cannot miss him: he does make our fire,
Fetch in our wood and serves in offices
That profit us. What, ho! slave! Caliban!
Thou earth, thou! speak.

CALIBAN

    [Within] There's wood enough within.

PROSPERO

    Come forth, I say! there's other business for thee:
Come, thou tortoise! when?

Re-enter ARIEL like a water nymph

    Fine apparition! My quaint Ariel,
Hark in thine ear.

DOUBLE MEANING ALERT!!!
Prospero calls Caliban dirt, but Shakespeare also hints here at Caliban's earthy instincts and desires. Here begins the "nature vs. nurture" debate. How important is a person's social and moral "training"?

ARIEL

    My lord it shall be done.

Exit

Presumably, Prospero whispers something in Ariel's ear.

PROSPERO

    Thou poisonous slave, got by the devil himself
Upon thy wicked dam, come forth!

Why don't you tell us how you really feel, Prospero?

dam = mother

Enter CALIBAN

CALIBAN

As wicked dew as e'er my mother brushed
With raven's feather from unwholesome fen
Drop on you both! a south-west blow on ye
And blister you all o'er!

PROSPERO

For this, be sure, tonight thou shalt have cramps,
Side-stitches that shall pen thy breath up; urchins
Shall, for that vast of night that they may work,
All exercise on thee; thou shalt be pinched
As thick as honeycomb, each pinch more stinging
Than bees that made 'em.

CALIBAN

     I must eat my dinner.
This island's mine, by Sycorax my mother,
Which thou tak'st from me. When thou cam'st first,
Thou strok'st me and made much of me, wouldst give me
Water with berries in't, and teach me how
To name the bigger light, and how the less,
That burn by day and night: and then I loved thee
And showed thee all the qualities o' th' isle,
The fresh springs, brine-pits, barren place and fertile:
Cursed be I that did so! All the charms
Of Sycorax, toads, beetles, bats, light on you!
For I am all the subjects that you have,
Which first was mine own king: and here you sty me
In this hard rock, whiles you do keep from me
The rest o' th' island.

PROSPERO

     Thou most lying slave,
Whom stripes may move, not kindness! I have used thee,
Filth as thou art, with humane care, and lodged thee
In mine own cell, till thou didst seek to violate
The honor of my child.

CALIBAN

O ho, O ho! would't had been done!
Thou didst prevent me; I had peopled else
This isle with Calibans.

MIRANDA

     Abhorred slave,
Which any print of goodness wilt not take,
Being capable of all ill! I pitied thee,
Took pains to make thee speak, taught thee each hour
One thing or other: when thou didst not, savage,
Know thine own meaning, but wouldst gabble like
A thing most brutish, I endowed thy purposes
With words that made them known. But thy vile race,
Though thou didst learn, had that in't which good natures

fen = bog, marsh

south-west = wind

Judging from Caliban's
response, the feeling's mutual!

Hint to Caliban: Avoid getting
into torture contests with
wizards who can deliver.

i.e., the sun and the moon

Wow! From father figure to
taskmaster.

What happened between
Prospero and Caliban?

sty = keep like a pig

stripes = lashes of a whip

Caliban, dude, are you crazy?!
You did WHAT to Miranda?! No
wonder they hate you!

One of the small debates of this
play is whether Shakespeare
wrote this line for Prospero or
Miranda. We pick Miranda.

No wonder Caliban speaks in
verse—Prospero and Miranda
taught him!

Could not abide to be with; therefore wast thou
Deservedly confined into this rock,
Who hadst deserved more than a prison.

CALIBAN

You taught me language; and my profit on't
Is, I know how to curse. The red plague rid you
For learning me your language!

PROSPERO

     Hag-seed, hence!
Fetch us in fuel; and be quick, thou'rt best,
To answer other business. Shrug'st thou, malice?
If thou neglect'st or dost unwillingly
What I command, I'll rack thee with old cramps,
Fill all thy bones with aches, make thee roar
That beasts shall tremble at thy din.

CALIBAN

     No, pray thee.

[Aside]

I must obey: his art is of such pow'r,
It would control my dam's god, Setebos,
and make a vassal of him.

PROSPERO

     So, slave; hence!

Exit CALIBAN

*Re-enter ARIEL, invisible, playing and singing;
FERDINAND following ARIEL'S song.*

Come unto these yellow sands,
And then take hands:
Curtsied when you have and kissed
The wild waves whist,
Foot it featly here and there;
And, sweet sprites, the burden bear.
Hark, hark!

Burden [dispersedly, within] Bow-wow

The watchdogs bark!

Burden Bow-wow

Hark, hark! I hear
The strain of strutting Chanticleer
Cry, cock-a-diddle-dow.

FERDINAND

Where should this music be? I' th' air or th' earth?
It sounds no more: and sure, it waits upon
Some god o' th' island. Sitting on a bank,
Weeping again the King my father's wrack,
This music crept by me upon the waters,
Allaying both their fury and my passion
With its sweet air: thence I have followed it,

More on the "nature vs. nurture" debate: Can a "base" nature be saved by TLC and the teaching of moral principles?

The red plague got its name from all the bleeding and sores it caused. Gross!

Translation (thou'rt best): It's in your best interest.

din = noise

Aside = for the audience's ears only

vassal = slave

Wow! That's some powerful magic!

whist = quiet

Foot it featly = dance smartly

"Who let the dog's out!?" Actually, "Bow-wow" is the back-up music, or "burden" for Ariel's song. (Who knew the Baha Men took tips from Shakespeare!?)

Prince Ferdinand (Ferdy) is having more than just a bad hair day. He barely survived a shipwreck and thinks he saw his father drown. At least the music on this island is good!

Or it hath drawn me rather. But 'tis gone.
No, it begins again.

ARIEL sings

Full fathom five thy father lies;
Of his bones are coral made;
Those are pearls that were his eyes:
Nothing of him that doth fade
But doth suffer a sea-change
Into something rich and strange.
Sea nymphs hourly ring his knell

Burden Ding-dong

Hark! now I hear them,–Ding-dong, bell.

FERDINAND
The ditty does remember my drowned father.
This is no mortal business, nor no sound
That the earth owes. I hear it now above me.

PROSPERO
The fringed curtains of thine eye advance
And say what thou seest yond.

MIRANDA
      What is't? a spirit?
Lord, how it looks about! Believe me, sir,
It carries a brave form. But 'tis a spirit.

PROSPERO
No, wench; it eats and sleeps and hath such senses
As we have, such. This gallant which thou seest
Was in the wrack; and, but he's something stained
With grief that's beauty's canker, thou mightst call him
A goodly person: he hath lost his fellows
And strays about to find 'em.

MIRANDA
      I might call him
A thing divine, for nothing natural
I ever saw so noble.

PROSPERO
[Aside] It goes on, I see,
As my soul prompts it. Spirit, fine spirit! I'll free thee
Within two days for this.

FERDINAND
      Most sure, the goddess
On whom these airs attend! Vouchsafe my prayer
May know if you remain upon this island;
And that you will some good instruction give
How I may bear me here: my prime request,
Which I do last pronounce, is, O you wonder!
If you be maid or no?

MIRANDA
      No wonder, sir;
But certainly a maid.

Great, Ariel, rub it in. Can't you sing about something a little more upbeat than drowned parents?

Notice yet another reference to the sea and how all things are changeable under its influence.

owes = owns

"fringed curtains" . . . Isn't that, like, eyelashes?

Twelve years on an island with only your father and Caliban to look at can make anyone seem like a god.

A canker is a worm that eats flowers.

Another aside: Ferdinand and Miranda are clueless as Prospero tells us their romance is all in his master plan.

Ferdinand sees Miranda here for the first time. Whoa baby!

Translation: Maybe this island isn't so bad—that is, if you're not a figment of my imagination.

Miranda misunderstands. She thinks Ferdinand is calling her chastity into question.

FERDINAND

        My language! heavens!
I am the best of them that speak this speech,
Were I but where 'tis spoken.

PROSPERO

        How? the best?
What wert thou, if the King of Naples heard thee?

FERDINAND

A single thing, as I am now, that wonders
To hear thee speak of Naples. He does hear me;
And that he does I weep: myself am Naples,
Who with mine eyes, never since at ebb, beheld
The King my father wracked.

MIRANDA

        Alack, for mercy!

FERDINAND

Yes, faith, and all his lords; the Duke of Milan
And his brave son being twain.

PROSPERO *[Aside]*

        The Duke of Milan
And his more braver daughter could control thee,
If now 'twere fit to do't. At the first sight
They have changed eyes. Delicate Ariel,
I'll set thee free for this.

To FERDINAND

A word, good sir;
I fear you have done yourself some wrong: a word.

MIRANDA

Why speaks my father so ungently? This
Is the third man that e'er I saw, the first
That e'er I sighed for: pity move my father
To be inclined my way!

FERDINAND

        O, if a virgin,
And your affection not gone forth, I'll make you
The Queen of Naples.

PROSPERO

Soft, sir! one word more.

[Aside]

They are both in either's pow'rs; but this swift business
I must uneasy make, lest too light winning
Make the prize light.

To FERDINAND

One word more; I charge thee
That thou attend me: thou dost here usurp
The name thou ow'st not; and hast put thyself
Upon this island as a spy, to win it
From me, the lord on't.

Translation: She's real, she's single, AND she speaks my language! Uh—did I mention I'm royalty?

Uh-oh. Ferdy's got to get past her father, first.

Thinking his father is dead, our man Ferdy thinks he's now the King of Naples. Shakespeare often has kings call themselves by their country, as in "myself am Naples."

Yep. Another aside. Notice how Prospero uses asides throughout the rest of the scene to fill the audience in on Prospero's plan for Miranda and Ferdinand.

They have changed eyes = they've fallen in love

That's right, Prospero! Show 'em who's in charge here.

e'er = ever

A marriage proposal?! That was quick! Can we say "impulsive"?

Looks like Prospero went to the University of No Pain, No Gain.

Should we give Prospero the Oscar for his performance as overbearing father or wait until the end of the play?

FERDINAND

No, as I am a man.

MIRANDA

There's nothing ill can dwell in such a temple:
If the ill spirit have so fair a house,
Good things will strive to dwell with't.

> Often people in Shakespeare's time thought beauty was more than just skin deep—pretty outside equaled pretty inside.

PROSPERO

To FERDINAND

Follow me.

To MIRANDA

Speak not you for him; he's a traitor.

To FERDINAND

Come;
I'll manacle thy neck and feet together:
Sea water shalt thou drink; thy food shall be
The fresh-brook mussels, withered roots and husks
Wherein the acorn cradled. Follow.

> Welcome to the island, Ferdinand!

FERDINAND

No;
I will resist such entertainment till
Mine enemy has more power.

> Entertainment? Hello?! More like torture. No wonder he tries to fight.

He draws, and is charmed from moving.

> Prospero's Rule #3: When all else fails, resort to wizardry.

MIRANDA

O dear father,
Make not too rash a trial of him, for
He's gentle and not fearful.

> DOUBLE MEANING ALERT!!! Gentle: 1) noble birth, as in "gentleman" 2) mild

PROSPERO

What? I say,
My foot my tutor? Put thy sword up, traitor;
Who mak'st a show but dar'st not strike, thy conscience
Is so possessed with guilt: come from thy ward,
For I can here disarm thee with this stick
And make thy weapon drop.

> foot = inferior

> "Ward" is a fencing posture.
> Aw, now he's just showing off.
> this stick = Prospero's staff, his magic wand

MIRANDA

Beseech you, father.

PROSPERO

Hence! hang not on my garments.

MIRANDA

Sir, have pity;
I'll be his surety.

> Translation: I'll vouch for him, Dad!

PROSPERO

Silence! one word more
Shall make me chide thee, if not hate thee. What!
An advocate for an imposter! hush!
Thou think'st there is no more such shapes as he,
Having seen but him and Caliban: foolish wench!
To th' most of men this is a Caliban
And they to him are angels.

> Hmm. The old "there are other fish in the sea" approach.

MIRANDA

    My affections
Are then most humble; I have no ambition
To see a goodlier man.

PROSPERO
To FERDINAND

Come on; obey:
Thy nerves are in their infancy again
And have no vigor in them.

FERDINAND

    So they are;
My spirits, as in a dream, are all bound up.
My father's loss, the weakness which I feel,
The wrack of all my friends, nor this man's threats,
To whom I am subdued, are but light to me,
Might I but through my prison once a day
Behold this maid: all corners else o' th' earth
Let liberty make use of; space enough
Have I in such a prison.

PROSPERO

[Aside] It works.

To FERDINAND

Come on.
Thou hast done well, fine Ariel!

To FERDINAND

Follow me.

To ARIEL

Hark what thou else shalt do me.

MIRANDA

    Be of comfort;
My father's of a better nature, sir,
Than he appears by speech: this is unwonted
Which now came from him.

PROSPERO

    Thou shalt be as free
As mountain winds: but then exactly do
All points of my command.

ARIEL

    To th' syllable.

PROSPERO
Come, follow. Speak not for him.

Exeunt

She's not biting.

Ferdinand will put up with anything as long as he can look at Miranda. Now THAT'S love. Or is it stupidity?

Antonio isn't the only one who knows to bribe. Prospero gets Ariel to do his bidding by promising Ariel freedom.

Translation: Don't take his side, Miranda.

Ferdinand, dude! Are you SURE you want this man for a father-in-law?!

Act I Notes

Act I Notes

Act I Notes

The Tempest

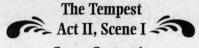

Act II, Scene I

Scene Synopsis

King Alonso is royally bummed about the shipwreck and about losing (or so he thinks) his son, Ferdinand, who was heir to the Naples throne. The King's brother, Sebastian, and his sidekick, Antonio (the same Antonio who stole Prospero's dukedom), foil all of Gonzalo's attempts to comfort the King. Ariel's magic music puts everyone to sleep except Sebastian and Antonio, who plot to kill King Alonso and Gonzalo in their sleep so that Sebastian can become King. Ariel returns in the nick of time, before they can carry out their plan.

Scene I

Another part of the island.

Enter ALONSO, SEBASTIAN, ANTONIO, GONZALO, ADRIAN, FRANCISCO, and others

GONZALO

    Beseech you, sir, be merry; you have cause,
    So have we all, of joy; for our escape
    Is much beyond our loss. Our hint of woe
    Is common; every day some sailor's wife,
    The masters of some merchant, and the merchant
    Have just our theme of woe; but for the miracle,
    I mean our preservation, few in millions
    Can speak like us: then wisely, good sir, weigh
    Our sorrow with our comfort.

> Translation: So we're shipwrecked on a desert island and your son is drowned. Look on the bright side, King Alonso—at least you're alive to mourn. Some comfort!

ALONSO

    Prithee, peace.

SEBASTIAN

    He receives comfort like cold porridge.

ANTONIO

    The visitor will not give him o'er so.

> In Shakespeare's time, a "visitor" was a church person who comforted the sick.

SEBASTIAN

    Look he's winding up the watch of his wit; by and by it will strike.

GONZALO

    Sir,—

> Comforting the King: Take Two

SEBASTIAN

    One: tell.

GONZALO

    When every grief is entertained that's offered,
    Comes to th' entertainer—

SEBASTIAN

    A dollar.

GONZALO

    Dolor comes to him, indeed: you have spoken truer than you purposed.

> Where are the pun police when you need them? "Entertainer" also means bartender, who can always use a dollar (but not a dolor, or sad mood!).

SEBASTIAN
You have taken it wiselier than I meant you should.

GONZALO
Therefore, my lord—

ANTONIO
Fie, what a spendthrift is he of his tongue!

ALONSO
I prithee, spare.

GONZALO
Well, I have done: but yet—

SEBASTIAN
He will be talking.

ANTONIO
Which, of he or Adrian, for a good
wager, first begins to crow?

SEBASTIAN
The old cock.

old cock = Gonzalo

ANTONIO
The cock'rel.

cockerel = Adrian, young rooster

SEBASTIAN
Done. The wager?

ANTONIO
A laughter.

They bet no money on who will speak first, only a laugh.

SEBASTIAN
A match!

ADRIAN
Though this island seem to be desert—

Adrian speaks first. Comforting the King: Take Three

ANTONIO
Ha, ha, ha!

SEBASTIAN
So, you're paid.

ADRIAN
Uninhabitable and almost inaccessible—

Uh . . . drawing attention to the island's bad points isn't helping, Adrian.

SEBASTIAN
Yet—

ADRIAN
Yet—

ANTONIO
He could not miss't.

ADRIAN
It must needs be of subtle, tender, and delicate
temperance.

ANTONIO
Temperance was a delicate wench.

Another pun: Temperance can refer to climate or a girl's name.

DOUBLE MEANING ALERT!!! (hubba,hubba!) "Delicate" and "subtle" are sexual references, too.

SEBASTIAN
Ay, and a subtle; as he most learnedly delivered.

ADRIAN

The air breathes upon us here most sweetly.

SEBASTIAN

As if it had lungs and rotten ones.

Sebastian and Antonio ought to enter the wisecrack Olympics.

ANTONIO

Or as 'twere perfumed by a fen.

GONZALO

Here is everything advantageous to life.

ANTONIO

True; save means to live.

SEBASTIAN

Of that there's none, or little.

GONZALO

How lush and lusty the grass looks! how green!

ANTONIO

The ground indeed is tawny.

tawny = a yellowish-brown color

SEBASTIAN

With an eye of green in't.

ANTONIO

He misses not much.

SEBASTIAN

No; he doth but mistake the truth totally.

GONZALO

But the rarity of it is,—which is indeed almost
beyond credit,—

SEBASTIAN

As many vouched rarities are.

GONZALO

That our garments, being, as they were,
Drenched in the sea, hold notwithstanding their
freshness and gloss, being rather new-dyed than
stained with salt water.

One of the advantages of washing up in an enchanted storm—the "tide" gets those hard-to-clean stains right out! (Hope the pun police aren't looking.)

ANTONIO

If but one of his pockets could speak, would it not
say he lies?

SEBASTIAN

Ay, or very falsely pocket up his report

H.E.T. Moment: "pocket up" is a metaphor for "take no notice of."

GONZALO

Methinks our garments are now as fresh as when we
put them on first in Afric, at the marriage of
the King's fair daughter Claribel to the King of Tunis.

Tunis is a town in Africa.

SEBASTIAN

'Twas a sweet marriage, and we prosper well in our return.

Do you detect a hint of sarcasm in Sebastian?

ADRIAN

Tunis was never graced before with such a paragon to
their queen.

paragon = perfection

GONZALO
Not since widow Dido's time.

ANTONIO
Widow! a pox o' that! How came that widow in? widow Dido!

SEBASTIAN
What if he had said 'widower Aeneas' too? Good Lord, how you take it!

ADRIAN
'Widow Dido' said you? you make me study of that: she was of Carthage, not of Tunis.

GONZALO
This Tunis, sir, was Carthage.

ADRIAN
Carthage?

GONZALO
I assure you, Carthage.

ANTONIO
His word is more than the miraculous harp.

SEBASTIAN
He hath raised the wall and houses too.

ANTONIO
What impossible matter will he make easy next?

SEBASTIAN
I think he will carry this island home in his pocket and give it his son for an apple.

ANTONIO
And, sowing the kernels of it in the sea, bring forth more islands.

GONZALO
Ay.

ANTONIO
Why, in good time.

GONZALO
Sir, we were talking that our garments seem now as fresh as when we were at Tunis at the marriage of your daughter, who is now Queen.

ANTONIO
And the rarest that e'er came there.

SEBASTIAN
Bate, I beseech you, widow Dido.

ANTONIO
O, widow Dido! ay, widow Dido.

GONZALO
Is not, sir, my doublet as fresh as the first day I wore it? I mean, in a sort.

Here's the skinny on the Dido jokes: Dido was a widow and ruler of Carthage. She fell in love with Aeneas, son of the love goddess Venus. He lived with Dido as the queen's consort. Then the god Mercury came to Aeneas and reminded him of his destiny—to found a new race of people (the Romans). Aeneas left Carthage and the broken-hearted Dido. What does all of this have to do with Ferdinand's sister's wedding? Almost four hundred years later, the jury is still out!

Mythology Check: The miraculous Harp of Amphion, which magically raised the walls of Thebes.

Give it a rest, Gonzalo! The clean-clothes routine isn't going to make the King feel better.

Bate = except for
Do these guys ever stop?

Hello?! A fresh doublet, maybe, but a stale argument.

ANTONIO

That sort was well fished for.

GONZALO

When I wore it at your daughter's marriage?

ALONSO

You cram these words into mine ears against
The stomach of my sense. Would I had never
Married my daughter there! for, coming thence,
My son is lost and, in my rate, she too,
Who is so far from Italy removed
I ne'er again shall see her. O thou mine heir
Of Naples and of Milan, what strange fish
Hath made his meal on thee?

That's right, Alonso. Nothing's worse than being force-fed comfort when your son is drowned (or so you think!).

FRANCISCO

Sir, he may live:
I saw him beat the surges under him,
And ride upon their backs; he trod the water,
Whose enmity he flung aside, and breasted
The surge most swol'n that met him; his bold head
'Bove the contentious waves he kept, and oared
Himself with his good arms in lusty stroke
To th' shore, that o'er his wave-worn basis bowed,
As stooping to relieve him: I not doubt
He came alive to land.

For once, Francisco has a lot to say.

enmity = hateful opposition

Hold up. Is this super swimmer the same guy who won the biggest wimp prize in the scene before?

ALONSO

No, no, he's gone.

SEBASTIAN

Sir, you may thank yourself for this great loss,
That would not bless our Europe with your daughter,
But rather lose her to an African;
Where she at least is banished from your eye,
Who hath cause to wet the grief on't.

Just what Alonso needs to hear, Sebastian, that the shipwreck is because he had to go to his daughter's wedding in Africa.

ALONSO

Prithee, peace.

SEBASTIAN

You were kneeled to and importuned otherwise
By all of us, and the fair soul herself
Weighed between loathness and obedience, at
Which end o' th' beam should bow. We have lost your son,
I fear, for ever: Milan and Naples have
More widows in them of this business' making
Than we bring men to comfort them:
The fault's your own.

You think maybe Sebastian was happy to marry his niece off to Antonio instead?

Great. Couldn't Alonso's own brother at least pretend to think Ferdinand's alive?

ALONSO

So is the dear'st o' th' loss.

GONZALO

My lord Sebastian,
The truth you speak doth lack some gentleness
And time to speak it in: you rub the sore,
When you should bring the plaster.

SEBASTIAN

    Very well.

ANTONIO

    And most chirurgeonly.

GONZALO

    It is foul weather in us all, good sir,
    When you are cloudy.

SEBASTIAN

    Foul weather?

ANTONIO

    Very foul.

GONZALO

    Had I plantation of this isle, my lord—

ANTONIO

    He'd sow't with nettle seed.

SEBASTIAN

        Or docks, or mallows.

GONZALO

    And were the king on't, what would I do?

SEBASTIAN

    Scape being drunk for want of wine.

GONZALO

    I' th' commonwealth I would by contraries
    Execute all things; for no kind of traffic
    Would I admit; no name of magistrate;
    Letters should not be known; riches, poverty,
    And use of service, none; contract, succession,
    Bourn, bound of land, tilth, vineyard, none;
    No use of metal, corn, or wine, or oil;
    No occupation; all men idle, all;
    And women too, but innocent and pure;
    No sovereignty.

SEBASTIAN

    Yet he would be king on't.

ANTONIO

    The latter end of his commonwealth forgets the beginning.

GONZALO

    All things in common nature should produce
    Without sweat or endeavor: treason, felony,
    Sword, pike, knife, gun, or need of any engine,
    Would I not have; but nature should bring forth,
    Of its own kind, all foison, all abundance,
    To feed my innocent people.

SEBASTIAN

    No marrying 'mong his subjects?

ANTONIO

    None, man; all idle: whores and knaves.

GONZALO

    I would with such perfection govern, sir,
    T' excel the golden age.

SEBASTIAN

    God his majesty!

Mythology Check: The Golden Age was a time of perfect peace—the Greeks' and Romans' equivalent of Eden before the Fall.

ANTONIO

    Long live Gonzalo!

GONZALO

    And—do you mark me, sir?

ALONSO

    Prithee, no more: thou dost talk nothing to me.

GONZALO

    I do well believe your Highness; and
    did it to minister occasion to these gentlemen,
    who are of such sensible and nimble lungs that
    they always use to laugh at nothing.

Hey—Gonzalo's joining the wisecrack competition!

ANTONIO

    'Twas you we laughed at.

GONZALO

    Who in this kind of merry fooling am nothing
    to you: so you may continue and laugh at
    nothing still.

Zing! Good one, Gonzalo.

ANTONIO

    What a blow was there given!

SEBASTIAN

    An it had not fall'n flatlong.

GONZALO

    You are gentlemen of brave mettle; you would lift
    the moon out of her sphere, if she would continue
    in it five weeks without changing.

Come on. Gonzalo's crack was sharper than the flat of a sword. (Oh – also, the word "an" is often used in place of "if" in Shakespeare.)

Enter ARIEL, invisible, playing solemn music

Here's Ariel again with that wild music.

SEBASTIAN

    We would so, and then go a-batfowling.

Batfowling is hunting birds in the moonlight with clubs. Yuck!

ANTONIO

    Nay, good my lord, be not angry.

GONZALO

    No, I warrant you; I will not adventure
    my discretion so weakly. Will you laugh
    me asleep, for I am very heavy?

adventure my discretion = risk my good name by getting mad at their lame jokes

ANTONIO

    Go sleep, and hear us.

Ariel's music must be very powerful—or snoringly boring!

All sleep except ALONSO, SEBASTIAN, and ANTONIO

ALONSO

    What, all so soon asleep! I wish mine eyes
    Would, with themselves, shut up my thoughts: I find
    They are inclined to do so.

SEBASTIAN

Please you, sir,
Do not omit the heavy offer of it:
It seldom visits sorrow; when it doth,
It is a comforter.

Translation: Go on. Catch a few Z's. Most mourners have insomnia.

ANTONIO

We two, my lord,
Will guard your person while you take your rest,
And watch your safety.

ALONSO

Thank you. Wondrous heavy.

Heavy, as in Alonso's eyelids.

ALONSO sleeps. Exit ARIEL

SEBASTIAN

What a strange drowsiness possesses them!

ANTONIO

It is the quality o' th' climate.

SEBASTIAN

Why
Doth it not then our eyelids sink? I find not
Myself disposed to sleep.

ANTONIO

Nor I; my spirits are nimble.
They fell together all, as by consent;
They dropped, as by a thunder-stroke. What might,
Worthy Sebastian? O, what might?–No more:–
And yet methinks I see it in thy face,
What thou shouldst be: th' occasion speaks thee, and
My strong imagination sees a crown
Dropping upon thy head.

Remember, Antonio stole Prospero's dukedom. Now watch the master manipulator work on Sebastian.

speaks thee = calls on you

SEBASTIAN

What, art thou waking?

ANTONIO

Do you not hear me speak?

SEBASTIAN

I do; and surely
It is a sleepy language and thou speak'st
Out of thy sleep. What is it thou didst say?
This is a strange repose, to be asleep
With eyes wide open; standing, speaking, moving,
And yet so fast asleep.

Gotta love all the ways Sebastian extends the theme of sleep. And listen to all the "s" sounds—is there a snake in the grass or what?

ANTONIO

Noble Sebastian,
Thou let'st thy fortune sleep–die, rather; wink'st
Whiles thou art waking.

Translation: You shut your eyes to your future while you are awake.

SEBASTIAN

Thou dost snore distinctly;
There's meaning in thy snores.

ANTONIO

    I am more serious than my custom: you
    Must be so too, if heed me; which to do
    Trebles thee o'er.

> Trebles thee o'er = makes you three times as great

SEBASTIAN

    Well, I am standing water.

> standing water = water with no movement

ANTONIO

    I'll teach you how to flow.

SEBASTIAN

    Do so: to ebb
    Hereditary sloth instructs me.

> "Hereditary sloth" means "natural laziness," or possibly Sebastian's problem of being second born (not able to be King).

ANTONIO

    O,
    If you but knew how you the purpose cherish
    Whiles thus you mock it! how, in stripping it,
    You more invest it! Ebbing men, indeed,
    Most often do so near the bottom run
    By their own fear or sloth.

> Keep hinting, Antonio. Sebastian's about to take the bait.

SEBASTIAN

    Prithee, say on:
    The setting of thine eye and cheek proclaim
    A matter from thee, and a birth indeed
    Which throes thee much to yield.

> A matter = important information

> Translation: Like a birth, what you need to tell me is difficult.

ANTONIO

    Thus, sir:
    Although this lord of weak remembrance, this,
    Who shall be of as little memory
    When he is earthed, hath here almost persuade,—
    For he's a spirit of persuasion, only
    Professes to persuade,—the King his son's alive,
    'Tis as impossible that he's undrowned
    As he that sleeps here swims.

> lord of weak remembrance, a.k.a. the sleeping Gonzalo

> earthed = buried

SEBASTIAN

    I have no hope
    That he's undrowned.

> OK, so Ferdy's dead (or so they think). What then?

ANTONIO

    O, out of that 'no hope'
    What great hope have you! no hope that way is
    Another way so high a hope that even
    Ambition cannot pierce a wink beyond,
    But doubt discovery there. Will you grant with me
    That Ferdinand is drowned?

> wink = glimpse

> Translation: What's in store for you is greater than anything you can imagine.

SEBASTIAN

    He's gone.

ANTONIO

    Then, tell me,
    Who's the next heir of Naples?

SEBASTIAN

      Claribel.

ANTONIO

      She that is Queen of Tunis; she that dwells
Ten leagues beyond man's life; she that from Naples
Can have no note, unless the sun were post—
The man i' th' moon's too slow—till newborn chins
Be rough and razorable; she that from whom?
We all were sea-swallowed, though some cast again,
And by that destiny to perform an act
Whereof what's past is prologue, what to come
In yours and my discharge.

SEBASTIAN

      What stuff is this! how say you?
'Tis true, my brother's daughter's Queen of Tunis;
So is she heir of Naples; 'twixt which regions
There is some space.

ANTONIO

      A space whose ev'ry cubit
Seems to cry out, 'How shall that Claribel
Measure us back to Naples? Keep in Tunis,
And let Sebastian wake.' Say, this were death
That now hath seized them; why, they were no worse
Than now they are. There be that can rule Naples
As well as he that sleeps; lords that can prate
As amply and unnecessarily
As this Gonzalo; I myself could make
A chough of as deep chat. O, that you bore
The mind that I do! what a sleep were this
For your advancement! Do you understand me?

SEBASTIAN

Methinks I do.

ANTONIO

      And how does your content
Tender your own good fortune?

SEBASTIAN

      I remember
You did supplant your brother Prospero.

ANTONIO

      True:
And look how well my garments sit upon me;
Much feater than before: my brother's servants
Were then my fellows; now they are my men.

SEBASTIAN

But, for your conscience?

ANTONIO

      Ay, sir; where lies that? if 'twere a kibe
'Twould put me to my slipper: but I feel not
This deity in my bosom: twenty consciences,

Ferdy's sister. Looks like Sebastian needs more than just a hint. Antonio's going to have to spell it out.

Translation: Claribel lives in the middle of nowhere, without web, fax, or phone!

Using the destiny argument AND all those theater puns (perform, act, past, prologue) to push Sebastian—this manipulator is good!

Finally, Sebastian is catching on. His niece, Claribel, is the new heir to the throne, but if something should—er—happen to her father, she couldn't get back to Naples easily.

So the idea now is death instead of sleep.

chough = jackdaw (a bird that talks)

Wink, wink; nudge, nudge.

Translation: And how do you like your "killer" luck? (Get the pun police!)

Prospero remembers, too.

feater = better, more stylin'

fellows = peers; men = servants

kibe = sore on the foot

That stand 'twixt me and Milan, candied be they
And melt ere they molest! Here lies your brother,
No better than the earth he lies upon,
If he were that which now he's like, that's dead;
Whom I, with this obedient steel, three inches of it,
Can lay to bed for ever; whiles you, doing thus,
To the perpetual wink for aye might put
This ancient morsel, this Sir Prudence, who
Should not upbraid our course. For all the rest,
They'll take suggestion as a cat laps milk;
They'll tell the clock to any business that
We say befits the hour.

SEBASTIAN
  Thy case, dear friend,
Shall be my precedent; as thou got'st Milan,
I'll come by Naples. Draw thy sword: one stroke
Shall free thee from the tribute which thou payest;
And I the King shall love thee.

ANTONIO
  Draw together;
And when I rear my hand, do you the like,
To fall it on Gonzalo.

SEBASTIAN
  O, but one word.

They talk apart

Re-enter ARIEL, invisible

ARIEL
My master through his art foresees the danger
That you, his friend, are in; and sends me forth–
For else his project dies–to keep them living.

Sings in GONZALO's ear

While you here do snoring lie,
Open-eyed conspiracy
His time doth take.
If of life you keep a care,
Shake off slumber, and beware:
Awake, awake!

ANTONIO
Then let us both be sudden.

GONZALO
  Now, good angels
Preserve the King.

They wake

ALONSO
Why, how now? ho, awake! Why are you drawn?
Wherefore this ghastly looking?

GONZALO
  What's the matter?

Yep, Antonio's the guiltless wonder. Now that he's duke, why worry about the past?

Obedient steel—isn't that, like, a knife?!

perpetual wink = eternal sleep

Antonio is referring to Gonzalo here.

Tribute? No wonder Antonio wants Sebastian to kill Alonso— no more protection payments.

Draw what? Portraits? No— their swords to do the deed!

Is Sebastian having second thoughts? Or does he want to know the best place to stab?

Prospero's master plan won't work if Alonso and Gonzalo die.

Saved by a song. Does Ariel have perfect timing or what?

They're drawn (at least their swords are) because they were about to kill you!

SEBASTIAN

Whiles we stood here securing your repose,
Even now, we heard a hollow burst of bellowing
Like bulls, or rather lions: did't not wake you?
It struck mine ear most terribly.

ALONSO

I heard nothing.

ANTONIO

O, 'twas a din to fright a monster's ear,
To make an earthquake! sure, it was the roar
Of a whole herd of lions.

ALONSO

Heard you this, Gonzalo?

GONZALO

Upon mine honor, sir, I heard a humming,
And that a strange one too, which did awake me:
I shaked you, sir, and cried: as mine eyes opened,
I saw their weapons drawn: there was a noise,
That's verily. 'Tis best we stand upon our guard,
Or that we quit this place; let's draw our weapons.

ALONSO

Lead off this ground; and let's make further search
For my poor son.

GONZALO

Heavens keep him from these beasts!
For he is, sure, i' th' island.

ALONSO

Lead away.

ARIEL

Prospero my lord shall know what I have done:
So, King, go safely on to seek thy son.

Exeunt

Liar, liar, pants on fire!

verily = true

Notice how the scene ends with two rhyming lines (a couplet). Our man Shakespeare often did this to tie the action up neatly.

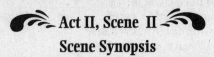

Act II, Scene II

Scene Synopsis

Caliban disses Prospero, then assumes the approaching thunderstorm is Prospero's punishment for his curses. Trinculo enters to get away from the storm and parks himself under Caliban's cloak. Stephano, who floated ashore on a barrel of wine, mistakes Caliban and Trinculo for a four-legged monster. As Stephano realizes his mistake and shares his wine with Caliban and Trinculo, Caliban decides Stephano must be a god. He vows to leave Prospero and serve his new master.

Scene II
Another part of the island.

Enter CALIBAN with a burden of wood. A noise of thunder heard

Remember how Prospero told Caliban to fetch wood in Act I? Well, he's doing it, but he's NOT happy about it.

CALIBAN

    All the infections that the sun sucks up
From bogs, fens, flats, on Prosper fall and make him
By inchmeal a disease! His spirits hear me
And yet I needs must curse. But they'll nor pinch,
Fright me with urchin–shows, pitch me i' th' mire,
Nor lead me, like a firebrand, in the dark
Out of my way, unless he bid 'em; but
For every trifle are they set upon me;
Sometime like apes that mow and chatter at me
And after bite me, then like hedgehogs which
Lie tumbling in my barefoot way and mount
Their pricks at my footfall; sometime am I
All wound with adders who with cloven tongues
Do hiss me into madness.

flats = low-level ground

inchmeal = inch by inch

urchin-shows = monsters
firebrand = flaming torch

mow = make faces

Looks like Prospero's a creative guy when it comes to tormenting folks. No wonder Caliban assumes the worst!

Enter TRINCULO

    Lo, now, lo!
Here comes a spirit of his, and to torment me
For bringing wood in slowly. I'll fall flat;
Perchance he will not mind me.

TRINCULO

    Here's neither bush nor shrub, to bear off
any weather at all, and another storm brewing;
I hear it sing i' th' wind: yond same black
cloud, yond huge one, looks like a foul
bombard that would shed his liquor. If it
should thunder as it did before, I know not
where to hide my head: yond same cloud cannot
choose but fall by pailfuls. What have we
here? a man or a fish? dead or alive? A fish:
he smells like a fish; a very ancient and fish-
like smell; a kind of not of the newest poor-
John. A strange fish! Were I in England now,
as once I was, and had but this fish painted,
not a holiday fool there but would give a piece

Shakesignal: In the way verse is often reserved for the high-born, prose is often used by the low-born and clowns.

bombard = leather flask

Note the foreshadowing of Trinculo's relationship to liquor. Drunkenness was a common comic device to Elizabethan audiences.

Poor-John was a salted fish enjoyed by Elizabethans.

of silver: there would this monster make a
man; any strange beast there makes a man:
when they will not give a doit to relieve a lame
beggar, they will lay out ten to see a dead Indian.
Legged like a man and his fins like arms!
Warm o' my troth! I do now let loose
my opinion; hold it no longer: this is no fish,
but an islander, that hath lately suffered by a
thunderbolt.

Thunder

Alas, the storm is come again! my best way is to
creep under his gaberdine; there is no other
shelter hereabouts: misery acquaints a man with
strange bed-fellows. I will here shroud till the
dregs of the storm be past.

Enter STEPHANO, singing: a bottle in his hand

STEPHANO

I shall no more to sea, to sea,
Here shall I die ashore–
This is a very scurvy tune to sing at a man's
funeral: well, here's my' comfort. [Drinks]

Sings

The master, the swabber, the boatswain and I,
The gunner and his mate
Loved Mall, Meg and Marian and Margery,
But none of us cared for Kate;
For she had a tongue with a tang,
Would cry to a sailor, Go hang!
She loved not the savor of tar nor of pitch,
Yet a tailor might scratch her wher'er she did itch:
Then to sea, boys, and let her go hang!
This is a scurvy tune too: but here's my comfort.

Drinks

CALIBAN

Do not torment me: Oh!

STEPHANO

What's the matter? Have we devils here? Do you put
tricks upon 's with savages and men of Inde, ha? I
have not scaped drowning to be afeard now of your
four legs; for it hath been said, As proper a man as
ever went on four legs cannot make him give ground;
and it shall be said so again while Stephano
breathes at nostrils.

CALIBAN

The spirit torments me; Oh!

STEPHANO

This is some monster of the isle with four legs, who
hath got, as I take it, an ague. Where the devil

"Make a man" means to make
a fortune.

doit = small coin

Another reference to the New
World: Native Americans were
brought back to England and
put in exhibitions.

gaberdine = cloak

Straight to the source—one of
Shakespeare's most famous
lines, spoken by a clown!

scurvy = vile, contemptible

A swabber is a sailor who
cleans the ship.

In joke? Kate's the shrew in
Shakespeare's *Taming of the
Shrew.*

tang = shrill sound

savor = smell

DOUBLE MEANING ALERT!!! The
tailor is doing a lot more than
just scratching!

men of Inde = people of the
West Indies

afeard = afraid

Seeing only Caliban's and
Trinculo's legs poking out from
under the cloak, Stephano
thinks he's found a monster.

Caliban thinks Trinculo is one of
Prospero's henchmen.

ague = fever

should he learn our language? I will give him some
relief, if it be but for that. if I can recover him
and keep him tame and get to Naples with him, he's a
present for any emperor that ever trod on neat's leather.

neat's leather = fine cowhide

CALIBAN

Do not torment me, prithee; I'll bring my wood home
faster.

STEPHANO

He's in his fit now and does not talk after the
wisest. He shall taste of my bottle: if he have
never drunk wine afore will go near to remove his
fit. If I can recover him and keep him tame, I will
not take too much for him; he shall pay for him that
hath him, and that soundly.

*"Take too much for him" means
the opposite of how it sounds.
Like Trinculo, Stephano talks of
selling Caliban for as much as
he can get.*

CALIBAN

Thou dost me yet but little hurt; thou wilt anon, I
know it by thy trembling: now Prosper works upon thee.

*Caliban mistakes Trinculo's
scared-to-death trembling for
Prospero's magic.*

STEPHANO

Come on your ways; open your mouth; here is that
which will give language to you, cat: open your
mouth; this will shake your shaking, I can tell you,
and that soundly: you cannot tell who's your friend:
open your chaps again.

*that which will give language =
liquor*

TRINCULO

I should know that voice: it should be—but he is
drowned; and these are devils: O defend me!

STEPHANO

Four legs and two voices: a most delicate monster!
His forward voice now is to speak well of his
friend; his backward voice is to utter foul speeches
and to detract. If all the wine in my bottle will
recover him, I will help his ague. Come. Amen! I
will pour some in thy other mouth.

TRINCULO

Stephano!

STEPHANO

Doth thy other mouth call me? Mercy, mercy! This is
a devil, and no monster: I will leave him; I have no
long spoon.

*An Elizabethan proverb taken
from The Canterbury Tales: "He
who eats with the devil should
use a long spoon."*

TRINCULO

Stephano! If thou beest Stephano, touch me and
speak to me: for I am Trinculo—be not afeard—thy
good friend Trinculo.

STEPHANO

If thou beest Trinculo, come forth: I'll pull thee
by the lesser legs: if any be Trinculo's legs,
these are they. Thou art very Trinculo indeed! How
cam'st thou to be the siege of this mooncalf? can
he vent Trinculos?

*Stephano asks if this "mooncalf"
(deformed creature) can fart
Trinculos.*

TRINCULO

I took him to be killed with a thunder-stroke. But
art thou not drowned, Stephano? I hope now thou art
not drowned. Is the storm overblown? I hid me
under the dead mooncalf's gaberdine for fear of
the storm. And art thou living, Stephano? O
Stephano, two Neapolitans scaped!

Hey! Watch the mooncalf stuff!
Monsters have feelings, too!

STEPHANO

Prithee, do not turn me about; my stomach is not constant.

Looks like Stephano has had
more liquor than he needs.

CALIBAN

[Aside] These be fine things, an if they be not sprites.
That's a brave god and bears celestial liquor.
I will kneel to him.

Sounds like Caliban's had too
much, too. He thinks Stephano
is a god!

STEPHANO

How didst thou scape? How cam'st thou hither?
swear by this bottle how thou cam'st hither. I
escaped upon a butt of sack which the sailors
heaved o'erboard, by this bottle; which I made of
the bark of a tree with mine own hands since I was
cast ashore.

A butt of sack is two hogsheads
of Spanish wine. That explains
why Stephano is tipsy!

CALIBAN

I'll swear upon that bottle to be thy true subject;
for the liquor is not earthly.

STEPHANO

Here; swear then how thou escapedst.

TRINCULO

Swum ashore. man, like a duck: I can swim like a
duck, I'll be sworn.

STEPHANO

Here, kiss the book. Though thou canst swim like a
duck, thou art made like a goose.

kiss the book = drink (which
makes Trinculo stagger)

Like a goose—Stephano
suggests Trinculo is standing on
wobbly legs.

TRINCULO

O Stephano. hast any more of this?

STEPHANO

The whole butt, man: my cellar is in a rock by th'
seaside where my wine is hid. How now, mooncalf!
how does thine ague?

CALIBAN

Hast thou not dropped from heaven?

STEPHANO

Out o' th' moon, I do assure thee: I was the Man i'
th' Moon when time was.

Being mistaken for a god has its
advantages. Stephano plays along.

CALIBAN

I have seen thee in her and I do adore thee:
My mistress showed me thee and thy dog and thy bush.

Hey Caliban! Did you know that
"gullible" isn't in the dictionary?
(And if you believe that, we've
got a bridge in Brooklyn to sell
you.)

STEPHANO

Come, swear to that; kiss the book: I will furnish
it anon with new contents swear.

furnish it anon = refill it

TRINCULO

By this good light, this is a very shallow monster!
I afeard of him! A very weak monster! The Man i'
th' Moon! A most poor credulous monster! Well
drawn, monster, in good sooth!

CALIBAN

I'll show thee every fertile inch o' th' island;
And I will kiss thy foot: I prithee, be my god.

TRINCULO

By this light, a most perfidious and drunken
monster! when 's god's asleep, he'll rob his bottle.

CALIBAN

I'll kiss thy foot; I'll swear myself thy subject.

STEPHANO

Come on then; down, and swear.

TRINCULO

I shall laugh myself to death at this puppy-headed
monster. A most scurvy monster! I could find in my
heart to beat him—

STEPHANO

Come, kiss.

TRINCULO

But that the poor monster's in drink: an abominable
monster!

CALIBAN

I'll show thee the best springs; I'll pluck thee berries;
I'll fish for thee and get thee wood enough.
A plague upon the tyrant that I serve!
I'll bear him no more sticks, but follow thee,
Thou wondrous man.

TRINCULO

A most ridiculous monster, to make a wonder of a
poor drunkard!

CALIBAN

I prithee, let me bring thee where crabs grow;
And I with my long nails will dig thee pignuts;
Show thee a jay's nest and instruct thee how
To snare the nimble marmoset; I'll bring thee
To clust'ring filberts and sometimes I'll get thee
Young scamels from the rock. Wilt thou go with me?

STEPHANO

I prithee now, lead the way without any more
talking. Trinculo, the King and all our company
else being drowned, we will inherit here: here;
bear my bottle: fellow Trinculo, we'll fill him by
and by again.

CALIBAN
Sings drunkenly

Farewell master; farewell, farewell!

Well drawn = that was a good
gulp

When Stephano isn't looking,
Trinculo thinks Caliban will
steal his liquor.

Judgment Call: Not that
Prospero's the greatest guy,
but does Caliban really want
to serve a drunk butler?

See, even Trinculo knows better!

pignuts = earth nuts; possibly
truffles, which pigs root out

A marmoset was a small,
supposedly edible monkey.

Scamels are believed to be
shellfish.

Stephano figures if he and
Trinculo are the only survivors,
they might as well be kings of
the island.

TRINCULO

    A howling monster: a drunken monster!

CALIBAN

    No more dams I'll make for fish

    Nor fetch in firing

    At requiring;

    Nor scrape trencher, nor wash dish

    'Ban, 'Ban, Ca-Caliban

    Has a new master: get a new man.

    Freedom, high-day! high-day, freedom! freedom,

    high-day, freedom!

Here "dams" are the kind that stop the flow of water.

Translation: Prospero, I QUIT!!

STEPHANO

    O brave monster! Lead the way.

Exeunt

Act II Notes

Act II Notes

Act II Notes

Act II Notes

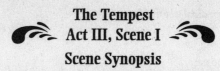

The Tempest
Act III, Scene I
Scene Synopsis

Ferdinand slaves for Prospero to get to Miranda—and thinks his reward will be worth the pains! Miranda visits her heartthrob and makes quick work of courtship, moving from introductions to marriage in just a few short lines! Unbeknownst to our lovebirds, daddy Prospero looks on, happy that the two have found each other.

Scene I
Before PROSPERO'S cell.

Enter FERDINAND, bearing a log

FERDINAND

There be some sports are painful, and their labor
Delight in them sets off: some kinds of baseness
Are nobly undergone and most poor matters
Point to rich ends. This my mean task
Would be as heavy to me as odious, but
The mistress which I serve quickens what's dead
And makes my labors pleasures: O, she is
Ten times more gentle than her father's crabbed,
And he's composed of harshness. I must remove
Some thousands of these logs and pile them up,
Upon a sore injunction: my sweet mistress
Weeps when she sees me work, and says, such baseness
Had never like executor. I forget:
But these sweet thoughts do even refresh my labors,
Most busy lest, when I do it.

Enter MIRANDA; and PROSPERO at a distance, unseen

MIRANDA

Alas, now, pray you,
Work not so hard: I would the lightning had
Burnt up those logs that you are enjoined to pile!
Pray, set it down and rest you: when this burns,
'Twill weep for having wearied you. My father
Is hard at study; pray now, rest yourself;
He's safe for these three hours.

FERDINAND

O most dear mistress,
The sun will set before I shall discharge
What I must strive to do.

MIRANDA

If you'll sit down,
I'll bear your logs the while: pray, give me that;
I'll carry it to the pile.

FERDINAND

No, precious creature;
I had rather crack my sinews, break my back,

Side notes:

Ferdy is attending Prospero's alma mater (the University of No Pain, No Gain).

That's for sure! But Ferdy has to go through Prospero to date his daughter.

injunction = command

Translation: Thoughts of his love are stronger (and more pleasant) the harder he works.

Just what our two lovebirds need, a parental spy watching their every move!

Weeping logs? Isn't that a little 'sappy?' Get it? (Get the pun police!)

That's what you think, Miranda!

Than you should such dishonor undergo,
While I sit lazy by.

MIRANDA

      It would become me
As well as it does you: and I should do it
With much more ease; for my good will is to it,
And yours it is against.

Who said chivalry is dead?

PROSPERO

Poor worm, thou art infected!
This visitation shows it.

Translation: Boy, honey, have you
got it bad!

MIRANDA

      You look wearily.

FERDINAND

No, noble mistress;'tis fresh morning with me
When you are by at night. I do beseech you—
Chiefly that I might set it in my prayers—
What is your name?

MIRANDA

      Miranda. O my father,
I have broke your hest to say so!

Oops! Note: Avoid letting Miranda
in on big secrets!

FERDINAND

      Admired Miranda!
Indeed the top of admiration! worth
What's dearest to the world! Full many a lady
I have eyed with best regard and many a time
Th' harmony of their tongues hath into bondage
Brought my too diligent ear: for several virtues
Have I liked several women; never any
With so full soul, but some defect in her
Did quarrel with the noblest grace she owed
And put it to the foil: but you, O you,
So perfect and so peerless, are created
Of every creature's best!

Notice the interplay here between
the words "admired" and
"Miranda." "Miranda" is related
to the Latin "mirare" meaning "to
admire."

Hmmm. So Ferdy's not a
beginner in romance.

Translation: Of all the women I've
liked, her good points never
totally outweighed her bad.

MIRANDA

      I do not know
One of my sex; no woman's face remember,
Save, from my glass, mine own; nor have I seen
More that I may call men than you, good friend,
And my dear father: how features are abroad,
I am skilless of; but, by my modesty,
The jewel in my dower, I would not wish
Any companion in the world but you,
Nor can imagination form a shape,
Besides yourself, to like of. But I prattle
Something too wildly and my father's precepts
I therein do forget.

glass = mirror

modesty, i.e., chastity

During the Renaissance, marriage
was often a business agreement;
a dower was the money a woman
brought to a union. The word
exists today as "dowry."

FERDINAND

      I am in my condition
A prince, Miranda; I do think, a king;

I would, not so!—and would no more endure
This wooden slavery than to suffer
The flesh fly blow my mouth. Hear my soul speak:
The very instant that I saw you, did
My heart fly to your service; there resides,
To make me slave to it; and for your sake
Am I this patient log–man.

MIRANDA
        Do you love me?

FERDINAND
        O heaven, O earth, bear witness to this sound
And crown what I profess with kind event
If I speak true! if hollowly, invert
What best is boded me to mischief! I
Beyond all limit of what else i' th' world
Do love, prize, honor you.

MIRANDA
        I am a fool
To weep at what I am glad of.

PROSPERO
        [Aside] Fair encounter
Of two most rare affections! Heavens rain grace
On that which breeds between 'em!

FERDINAND
        Wherefore weep you?

MIRANDA
        At mine unworthiness that dare not offer
What I desire to give, and much less take
What I shall die to want. But this is trifling;
And all the more it seeks to hide itself,
The bigger bulk it shows. Hence, bashful cunning!
And prompt me, plain and holy innocence!
I am your wife, it you will marry me;
If not, I'll die your maid: to be your fellow
You may deny me; but I'll be your servant,
Whether you will or no.

FERDINAND
        My mistress, dearest;
And I thus humble ever.

MIRANDA
        My husband, then?

FERDINAND
        Ay, with a heart as willing
As bondage e'er of freedom: here's my hand.

MIRANDA
        And mine, with my heart in't; and now farewell
Till half an hour hence.

FERDINAND
        A thousand thousand!

He wishes it weren't the case and that his dad was still alive.

A flesh fly feeds on flesh and deposits her eggs in it—eeyew!

Looks like Shakespeare believed in love at first sight!

Just come right out and ask him, Miranda!

H.E.T. Moment: personification of heaven and earth

At least Dad is happy.

Obviously there are no books on dating on this island. Miranda has barely introduced herself and now they're talking marriage again!

Ferdy's heart wants Miranda like bondage wants freedom.

(Farewells, that is.)

Exeunt FERDINAND and MIRANDA severally

They go in separate directions.

PROSPERO

> So glad of this as they I cannot be,
> Who are surprised withal; but my rejoicing
> At nothing can be more. I'll to my book,
> For yet ere supper time must I perform
> Much business appertaining.

So Prospero knew all along
they'd hook up—all a part of the
master plan!

Exit

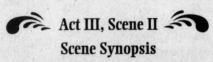

Act III, Scene II

Scene Synopsis

Our three drunk stooges stumble across the island. Caliban and Trinculo have "issues," which Ariel uses to his own advantage when he does a ventriloquist act on the clueless Trinculo. Caliban asks Stephano to kill Prospero and marry Miranda; Stephano blindly agrees. Super-Spirit Ariel overhears the murderous plot and distracts the three clowns with drum tunes.

Scene II

Another part of the island.

Enter CALIBAN, STEPHANO, and TRINCULO

STEPHANO

> Tell not me; when the butt is out, we will drink
> water; not a drop before: therefore bear up, and
> board 'em. Servant monster, drink to me.

They won't drink anything but
wine until they run out.

TRINCULO

> Servant monster! the folly of this island! They
> say there's but five upon this isle: we are three
> of them; if th' other two be brained like us, the
> state totters.

brained = drunk

STEPHANO

> Drink, servant monster, when I bid thee: thy eyes
> are almost set in thy head.

TRINCULO

> Where should they be set else? he were a brave
> monster indeed, if they were set in his tail.

STEPHANO

> My man-monster hath drowned his tongue in sack:
> for my part, the sea cannot drown me; I swam, ere I
> could recover the shore, five-and-thirty leagues off
> and on. By this light, thou shalt be my lieutenant,
> monster, or my standard.

standard = flag-bearer

TRINCULO

> Your lieutenant, if you list; he's no standard.

list = desire . . . Also, another
pun: Caliban is so drunk he can't
stand (much less bear a flag).

STEPHANO

> We'll not run, Monsieur Monster.

TRINCULO

Nor go neither; but you'll lie like dogs and yet say
nothing neither.

STEPHANO

Mooncalf, speak once in thy life, if thou beest a
good mooncalf.

CALIBAN

How does thy honor? Let me lick thy shoe.
I'll not serve him; he's not valiant.

TRINCULO

Thou liest, most ignorant monster: I am in case to
justle a constable. Why, thou deboshed fish thou,
was there ever man a coward that hath drunk so much
sack as I today? Wilt thou tell a monstrous lie,
being but half a fish and half a monster?

CALIBAN

Lo, how he mocks me! wilt thou let him, my lord?

TRINCULO

'Lord' quoth he! That a monster should be such a natural!

CALIBAN

Lo, lo, again! bite him to death, I prithee.

STEPHANO

Trinculo, keep a good tongue in your head: if you
prove a mutineer,—the next tree! The poor monster's
my subject and he shall not suffer indignity.

CALIBAN

I thank my noble lord. Wilt thou be pleased to
hearken once again to the suit I made to thee?

STEPHANO

Marry, will I
kneel and repeat it; I will stand,
and so shall Trinculo.

Enter ARIEL, invisible

CALIBAN

As I told thee before, I am subject to a tyrant, a
sorcerer, that by his cunning hath cheated me
of the island.

ARIEL

Thou liest.

CALIBAN

Thou liest, thou jesting monkey, thou: I would my
valiant master would destroy thee! I do not lie.

STEPHANO

Trinculo, if you trouble him any more in's tale, by
this hand, I will supplant some of your teeth.

TRINCULO

Why, I said nothing.

Rumor has it that the "run" and "go" references have to do with urination.

Again with the mooncalf stuff!

Caliban won't serve Trinculo.

in case = in the form to

deboshed = debauched, drunken

Notice how Caliban tries to manipulate Stephano's loyalty.

such a natural = natural idiot

"the next tree": Mutineers were executed by hanging from trees.

suit = petition or request

So now it's Caliban's side of the Prospero story.

Caliban thinks Trinculo said he lied (not Ariel) and addresses this line to him.

STEPHANO

> Mum, then, and no more. *[To CALIBAN]* Proceed.

Mum's the word—meaning quiet.

CALIBAN

> I say, by sorcery he got this isle;
> From me he got it. if thy greatness will
> Revenge it on him,—for I know thou dar'st,
> But this thing dare not,—

this thing = Trinculo

STEPHANO

> That's most certain.

CALIBAN

> Thou shalt be lord of it and I'll serve thee.

STEPHANO

> How now shall this be compassed?
> Canst thou bring me to the party?

Party? Who's having a party?
Actually "party" here means person, specifically Prospero.

CALIBAN

> Yea, yea, my lord: I'll yield him thee asleep,
> Where thou mayst knock a nail into his head.

Ouch! Prospero, look out!

ARIEL

> Thou liest; thou canst not.

Invisibility: a practical joker's dream come true.

CALIBAN

> What a pied ninny's this! Thou scurvy patch!
> I do beseech thy greatness, give him blows
> And take his bottle from him: when that's gone
> He shall drink naught but brine; for I'll not show him
> Where the quick freshes are.

pied ninny = patched fool (probably referring to Trinculo's jester outfit)

brine = salty water
quick freshes = freshwater springs

STEPHANO

> Trinculo, run into no further danger:
> interrupt the monster one word further, and,
> by this hand, I'll turn my mercy out o' doors
> and make a stockfish of thee.

stockfish = a fish that was beaten before it was cooked

TRINCULO

> Why, what did I? I did nothing. I'll go farther off.

STEPHANO

> Didst thou not say he lied?

ARIEL

> Thou liest.

STEPHANO

> Do I so? take thou that.

Beats TRINCULO

> As you like this, give me the lie another time.

TRINCULO

> I did not give the lie. Out o' your
> wits and hearing too? A pox o' your bottle!
> this can sack and drinking do. A murrain on
> your monster, and the devil take your fingers!

"Murrain" is kind of like Mad Cow's disease. Good thing Trinculo doesn't have the power to make his curses come true!

CALIBAN

> Ha, ha, ha!

STEPHANO

Now, forward with your tale. Prithee, stand
further off.

CALIBAN

Beat him enough: after a little time
I'll beat him too.

STEPHANO

Stand farther. Come, proceed.

CALIBAN

Why, as I told thee, 'tis a custom with him,
I' th' afternoon to sleep: there thou mayst brain him,
Having first seized his books, or with a log
Batter his skull, or paunch him with a stake   paunch = stab
Or cut his wesand with thy knife. Remember   wesand = windpipe
First to possess his books; for without them
He's but a sot, as I am, nor hath not   Caliban knows Prospero's powers
One spirit to command: they all do hate him   come from his books, not his
As rootedly as I. Burn but his books.   natural ability.
He has brave utensils,–for so he calls them–   brave utensils = cool household stuff
Which when he has a house, he'll deck withal
And that most deeply to consider is
The beauty of his daughter; he himself
Calls her a nonpareil: I never saw a woman,   nonpareil = unequaled person
But only Sycorax my dam and she;
But she as far surpasseth Sycorax
As great'st does least.

STEPHANO

Is it so brave a lass?

CALIBAN

Ay, lord; she will become thy bed, I warrant.   Uh, Caliban, do you think Miranda
And bring thee forth brave brood.   might want to make her own
decision about who to marry?

STEPHANO

Monster, I will kill this man: his daughter and I
will be king and queen–save our Graces!–and
Trinculo and thyself shall be viceroys. Dost thou   viceroys = substitute kings
like the plot, Trinculo?

TRINCULO

Excellent.

STEPHANO

Give me thy hand: I am sorry I beat thee; but,
while thou liv'st, keep a good tongue in thy head.

CALIBAN

Within this half hour will he be asleep:
Wilt thou destroy him then?

STEPHANO

Ay, on mine honor.

ARIEL

This will I tell my master.   FBI Surveillance has got nothing on
this spirit!

CALIBAN

Thou mak'st me merry; I am full of pleasure:
Let us be jocund: will you troll the catch
You taught me but whilere?

jocund = happy
troll the catch = sing the song

STEPHANO

At thy request, monster, I will do reason, any
reason. Come on, Trinculo, let us sing.

Sings

Flout 'em and scout 'em
And scout 'em and flout 'em
Thought is free.

Not exactly one of Shakespeare's
greatest hits!

CALIBAN

That's not the tune.

Ariel plays the tune on a tabor and pipe

A one-spirit band with a small
drum and flute!

STEPHANO

What is this same?

TRINCULO

This is the tune of our catch, played by the picture
of Nobody.

Nobody you can see, at least!

STEPHANO

If thou beest a man, show thyself in thy likeness:
if thou beest a devil, take't as thou list.

If the voice belongs to a devil,
he/she can take any form it pleases.

TRINCULO

O, forgive me my sins!

STEPHANO

He that dies pays all debts: I defy thee. Mercy upon us!

"He that dies pays all debts" is a
proverb from Shakespeare's time.

CALIBAN

Art thou afeard?

STEPHANO

No, monster, not I.

CALIBAN

Be not afeard; the isle is full of noises,
Sounds and sweet airs, that give delight and hurt not.
Sometimes a thousand twangling instruments
Will hum about mine ears, and sometimes voices
That, if I then had waked after long sleep,
Will make me sleep again: and then, in dreaming,
The clouds methought would open and show riches
Ready to drop upon me that, when I waked,
I cried to dream again.

In one of the most poetic speeches
of the play, Caliban (who only sixty
lines ago was talking about
"braining" Prospero) eloquently
describes the beauty of the island.
Like Prospero, who alternates from
tyrant to wronged duke to loving
father, Caliban has different sides
to his personality. Are these people
complicated or what?

STEPHANO

This will prove a brave kingdom to me, where I shall
have my music for nothing.

CALIBAN

When Prospero is destroyed.

STEPHANO

That shall be by and by: I remember the story.

TRINCULO

The sound is going away; let's follow it, and
after do our work.

STEPHANO

Lead, monster; we'll follow. I would I could see
this taborer; he lays it on. Wilt come?

TRINCULO

I'll follow, Stephano.

Exeunt

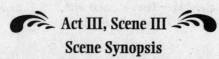

Act III, Scene III

Scene Synopsis

King Alonso and the gang are pooped from looking for Ferdinand and give him up for dead. Ariel
teases everyone with a fake feast and then appears to Alonso, Sebastian, and Antonio as a harpy,
reminding them of their roles in Prospero's banishment from Milan. Ariel's award-winning performance
leaves the three usurpers one fry short of a Happy Meal. Gonzalo sends Francisco and Adrian to protect
Alonso and our two villains from themselves.

Scene III

Another part of the island.

*Enter ALONSO, SEBASTIAN, ANTONIO, GONZALO,
ADRIAN, FRANCISCO, and others*

GONZALO

By'r Lakin, I can go no further, sir;
My old bones ache: here's a maze trod indeed
Through forthrights and meanders! By your patience,
I needs must rest me.

"By'r Lakin" is a squished together
"By our ladykin." (Virgin Mary)

forthrights and meanders =
straight paths and curvy

ALONSO

Old lord, I cannot blame thee,
Who am myself attached with weariness,
To th' dulling of my spirits: sit down, and rest.
Even here I will put off my hope and keep it
No longer for my flatterer: he is drowned
Whom thus we stray to find, and the sea mocks
Our frustrate search on land. Well, let him go.

Translation: I'll stop flattering
myself with hope. My son is gone.

ANTONIO

[Aside to SEBASTIAN] I am right glad that he's so out of hope.
Do not, for one repulse, forgo the purpose
That you resolved t' effect.

SEBASTIAN

[Aside to ANTONIO] The next advantage
Will we take throughly.

If at first you don't succeed (in
killing the King), try, try again!

ANTONIO

[Aside to SEBASTIAN] Let it be tonight;

For, now they are oppressed with travel, they
Will not, nor cannot, use such vigilance
As when they are fresh.

SEBASTIAN

[Aside to ANTONIO] I say, tonight: no more.

Solemn and strange music

Music—must be some magic
coming on!

ALONSO

What harmony is this? My good friends, hark!

GONZALO

Marvelous sweet music!

*Enter PROSPERO above, invisible. Enter several strange
Shapes, bringing in a banquet; they dance about it with
gentle actions of salutation; and, inviting the King, &c.
to eat, they depart*

shapes, i.e., spirits

ALONSO

Give us kind keepers, heavens! What were these?

SEBASTIAN

A living drollery. Now I will believe
That there are unicorns, that in Arabia
There is one tree, the phoenix' throne, one phoenix
At this hour reigning there.

living drollery = a puppet show
come to life

Sebastian says he'll believe the
other far-fetched travelers' tales
he's heard.

ANTONIO

I'll believe both;
And what does else want credit, come to me,
And I'll be sworn 'tis true: travelers ne'er did lie,
Though fools at home condemn 'em.

GONZALO

If in Naples
I should report this now, would they believe me?
If I should say, I saw such islanders–
For, certes, these are people of the island–
Who, though they are of monstrous shape, yet, note,
Their manners are more gentle-kind than of
Our human generation you shall find
Many, nay, almost any.

certes = certain

PROSPERO

[Aside] Honest lord,
Thou hast said well; for some of you there present
Are worse than devils.

Three guesses who Prospero is
talking about! (Alonso, Antonio,
and Sebastian.)

ALONSO

I cannot too much muse
Such shapes, such gesture and such sound, expressing,
Although they want the use of tongue, a kind
Of excellent dumb discourse.

muse = wonder at

PROSPERO

[Aside]

Praise in departing.

This is a proverb, meaning "wait
until something ends to decide
what you think."

FRANCISCO

They vanished strangely.

Congratulations! You've found Francisco's only other line!

SEBASTIAN

No matter, since
They have left their viands behind; for we have stomachs.
Will't please you taste of what is here?

viands = food

ALONSO

Not I.

Who knows what they put in the food here?

GONZALO

Faith, sir, you need not fear. When we were boys,
Who would believe that there were mountaineers
Dewlapped like bulls, whose throats had hanging at 'em
Wallets of flesh? or that there were such men
Whose heads stood in their breasts? which now we find
Each putter-out of five for one will bring us
Good warrant of.

These travelers' tales hit both extremes: people with lots of neck (flaps) and people with no necks!

In Shakespeare's time, travel was so dangerous, travelers put down a sum for insurance and made five times the amount if they made it back alive.

ALONSO

I will stand to and feed,
Although my last: no matter, since I feel
The best is past. Brother, my lord the Duke,
Stand to and do as we.

Thunder and lightning. Enter ARIEL, like a harpy; claps his wings upon the table; and, with a quaint device, the banquet vanishes

Harpy: a big black felt-tip pen—wait! That's a Sharpie! A harpy is a bird with the head of a woman who took travelers' food and uttered dire prophecies.

ARIEL

You are three men of sin, whom destiny,
That hath to instrument this lower world
And what is in't, the never-surfeited sea
Hath caused to belch up you; and on this island
Where man doth not inhabit; you 'mongst men
Being most unfit to live. I have made you mad;
And even with such-like valor men hang and drown
Their proper selves.

Notice that Ariel speaks only to Alonso, Sebastian, and Antonio. The others don't hear or see him.

Translation: Fate has caused the sea to spit you out on this island even though you aren't fit to live.

ALONSO, SEBASTIAN &c. draw their swords

You fools! I and my fellows
Are ministers of Fate: the elements,
Of whom your swords are tempered, may as well
Wound the loud winds, or with bemocked-at stabs
Kill the still-closing waters, as diminish
One dowle that's in my plume: my fellow ministers
Are like invulnerable. If you could hurt,
Your swords are now too massy for your strengths
And will not be uplifted. But remember–
For that's my business to you–that you three
From Milan did supplant good Prospero;
Exposed unto the sea, which hath requit it,
Him and his innocent child: for which foul deed
The powers, delaying, not forgetting, have
Incensed the seas and shores, yea, all the creatures,
Against your peace. Thee of thy son, Alonso,

tempered = made hard by cooling

Their swords are powerless against Ariel's extra-strength magic.

dowle = small feather

massy = heavy

Just a not-so-gentle reminder of their treachery!

They have bereft; and do pronounce by me:
Ling'ring perdition, worse than any death
Can be at once, shall step by step attend
You and your ways; whose wraths to guard you from
Which here, in this most desolate isle, else falls
Upon your heads—is nothing but heart's sorrow
And a clear life ensuing.

*He vanishes in thunder; then, to soft music enter the Shapes
again, and dance, with mocks and mows, and carrying out
the table*

PROSPERO

    Bravely the figure of this harpy hast thou
Performed, my Ariel; a grace it had, devouring:
Of my instruction hast thou nothing bated
In what thou hadst to say: so, with good life
And observation strange, my meaner ministers
Their several kinds have done. My high charms work
And these mine enemies are all knit up
In their distractions; they now are in my power;
And in these fits I leave them, while I visit
Young Ferdinand, whom they suppose is drowned,
And his and mine loved darling.

Exit above

GONZALO

    I' th' name of something holy, sir, why stand you
In this strange stare?

ALONSO

        O, it is monstrous, monstrous:
Methought the billows spoke and told me of it;
The winds did sing it to me, and the thunder,
That deep and dreadful organ pipe, pronounced
The name of Prosper: it did bass my trespass.
Therefore my son i' th' ooze is bedded, and
I'll seek him deeper than e'er plummet sounded
And with him there lie mudded.

Exit

SEBASTIAN

    But one fiend at a time,
I'll fight their legions o'er.

ANTONIO

    I'll be thy second.

Exeunt SEBASTIAN, and ANTONIO

GONZALO

    All three of them are desperate: their great guilt,
Like poison given to work a great time after,
Now gins to bite the spirits. I do beseech you
That are of suppler joints, follow them swiftly

If we ever need grudge-holding lessons, we know whose boss to call.

Ling'ring perdition = sl-o-o-o-w torture

heart's sorrow = regret

clear = blameless

Prospero applauds Ariel's work in making the banquet vamoose!

bated = left out

Gotta love it when a good plan comes together! (Wait—can we really call sending your enemies into fits a "good" plan?)

Easy for you to say, Gonzalo—you didn't see a thing!

"Bass my trespass" means to sound with a deep and full voice all of Alonso's sins.

Wow! The harpy gag really worked! Alonso's ready to drown himself . . .

. . . unlike Sebastian and Antonio, who want to fight. (Good luck winning against these odds, dudes.)

Desperate—you can say that again! (Oh, we just did.)

"you that are of suppler joints," i.e., Adrian and Francisco

And hinder them from what this ecstasy   ecstasy = fit of madness
May now provoke them to.

ADRIAN

Follow, I pray you.

Exeunt

Act III Notes

Act III Notes

Act III Notes

The Tempest
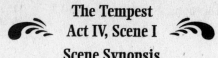
Act IV, Scene I
Scene Synopsis

Prospero gives his blessing to Miranda and Ferdinand and whips up a magic show for them that would put Vegas magicians to shame. He cuts the party short when he remembers Caliban, Stephano, and Trinculo are coming to kill him, and sends everyone away in a hurry. With the help of the ever-efficient Ariel, Prospero uses flashy clothes to lure our three clowns into a trap where they are hunted (and bitten!) by imaginary dogs. Prospero has everyone exactly where he wants them!

Scene I
Before PROSPERO'S cell.

Enter PROSPERO, FERDINAND, and MIRANDA

PROSPERO

If I have too austerely punished you,
Your compensation makes amends, for I
Have given you here a third of mine own life,
Or that for which I live; who once again
I tender to thy hand: all thy vexations
Were but my trials of thy love and thou
Hast strangely stood the test here, afore heaven,
I ratify this my rich gift. O Ferdinand,
Do not smile at me that I boast her off,
For thou shalt find she will outstrip all praise
And make it halt behind her.

FERDINAND

    I do believe it
Against an oracle.

PROSPERO

Then, as my gift and thine own acquisition
Worthily purchased take my daughter: but
If thou dost break her virgin-knot before
All sanctimonious ceremonies may
With full and holy rite be minist'red,
No sweet aspersion shall the heavens let fall
To make this contract grow: but barren hate,
Sour-eyed disdain and discord shall bestrew
The union of your bed with weeds so loathly
That you shall hate it both: therefore take heed,
As Hymen's lamp shall light you.

FERDINAND

    As I hope
For quiet days, fair issue and long life,
With such love as 'tis now, the murkiest den,
The most opportune place, the strong'st suggestion.
Our worser genius can, shall never melt
Mine honor into lust, to take away
The edge of that day's celebration

---

austerely = harshly

The third of Prospero's own life is his daughter.

Looks like Ferdy made it through UNPNG (University of No Pain, No Gain)!

ratify = confirm, sanction

An oracle is a soothsayer. Ferdy says he'll believe what Prospero just said even if an oracle denies it.

No hanky-panky before the wedding day, or Ferdinand will have to answer to all the magic Miranda's father can muster!

Mythology Check: Hymen was the god of the wedding feast.

fair issue = good-looking offspring

Ferdy says he'll resist the sexiest situation nature can devise!

When I shall think: or Phoebus' steeds are foundered,
Or Night kept chained below.

PROSPERO

Fairly spoke.
Sit then and talk with her; she is thine own.
What, Ariel! my industrious servant, Ariel!

Enter ARIEL

ARIEL

What would my potent master? here I am.

PROSPERO

Thou and thy meaner fellows your last service
Did worthily perform; and I must use you
In such another trick. Go bring the rabble,
O'er whom I give thee pow'r, here to this place:
Incite them to quick motion; for I must
Bestow upon the eyes of this young couple
Some vanity of mine art: it is my promise,
And they expect it from me.

ARIEL

Presently?

PROSPERO

Ay, with a twink.

ARIEL

Before you can say 'come' and 'go,'
And breathe twice and cry 'so, so,'
Each one, tripping on his toe,
Will be here with mop and mow.
Do you love me, master? no?

PROSPERO

Dearly my delicate Ariel. Do not approach
Till thou dost hear me call.

ARIEL

Well, I conceive.

Exit

PROSPERO

Look thou be true; do not give dalliance
Too much the rein: the strongest oaths are straw
To th' fire i' th' blood: be more abstemious,
Or else, good night your vow!

FERDINAND

I warrant you sir;
The white cold virgin snow upon my heart
Abates the ardor of my liver.

PROSPERO

Well.
Now come, my Ariel! bring a corollary,
Rather than want a spirit: appear and pertly!
No tongue! all eyes! be silent.

Mythology Check again: Phoebus is another name for Apollo, god of the Sun.

Translation: Permission granted!

meaner = humbler or lower

the rabble = Ariel's "quality" (gang)

Prospero's Rule #4: When you want to impress people, pull out all the magical stops. Looks like a big show is in the works!

A lot of "mowing" (face-making) goes on this play, doesn't it?

conceive = understand

Leave Ferdy and Miranda alone for two minutes and already the chastity oaths are in jeopardy! Looks like Dad is interrupting a major mash session.

Promises, promises! But can Ferdy keep his hands to himself until they marry?

corollary = surplus

A Masque, Enter IRIS

IRIS

> Ceres, most bounteous lady, thy rich leas
> Of wheat, rye, barley, vetches, oats and pease;
> Thy turfy mountains, where live nibbling sheep,
> And flat meads thatched with stover, them to keep;
> Thy banks with pioned and twilled brims,
> Which spongy April at thy hest betrims,
> To make cold nymphs chaste crowns; and thy
>   broom groves,
> Whose shadow the dismissed bachelor loves,
> Being lasslorn: thy pole-clipt vineyard;
> And thy sea-marge, sterile and rocky-hard,
> Where thou, thyself dost air;—the queen o' th' sky,
> Whose wat'ry arch and messenger am I,
> Bids thee leave these, and with her sovereign grace,
> Here on this grass-plot, in this very place,
> To come and sport: her peacocks fly amain:
> Approach, rich Ceres, her to entertain.

Enter CERES

CERES

> Hail, many-color'd messenger, that ne'er
> Dost disobey the wife of Jupiter;
> Who with thy saffron wings upon my flow'rs
> Diffusest honey drops, refreshing show'rs,
> And with each end of thy blue bow dost crown
> My bosky acres and my unshrubbed down,
> Rich scarf to my proud earth; why hath thy queen
> Summoned me hither, to this short-grassed green?

IRIS

> A contract of true love to celebrate;
> And some donation freely to estate
> On the blessed lovers.

CERES

>   Tell me, heavenly bow,
> If Venus or her son, as thou dost know,
> Do now attend the queen? Since they did plot
> The means that dusky Dis my daughter got,
> Her and her blind boy's scandalled company
> I have forsworn.

IRIS

>   Of her society
> Be not afraid: I met her Deity
> Cutting the clouds towards Paphos and her son
> Dove-drawn with her. Here thought they to have done
> Some wanton charm upon this man and maid,
> Whose vows are, that no bed-right shall be paid
> Till Hymen's torch be lighted: but in vain;
> Mars's hot minion is returned again;

A masque is a show based on mythology or allegory.

leas = meadows

Mythology Check: Iris was the female messenger of the gods.

mead = grassy lowland;
stover = dried feed;
pioned and twilled brims = woven branches

broom groves = bushes of gorse

pole-clipt = trimmed

sea-marge = ocean bank

Mythology Check: The "queen o' th' sky" is Juno (Iris works for her).

The peacock was Juno's sacred symbol.

Mythology Check: Ceres was goddess of agriculture and sister-in-law of Juno.

More Mythology: Iris' symbol is the rainbow; Juno is married to Jupiter.

bosky = wooded

estate = give, present

What's the low-down on this goddess gossip? Ceres is giving Venus, Juno's attendant, the silent treatment because Venus helped kidnap Ceres' daughter. Ceres hopes Venus isn't going to show up at this party.

Ceres may not have to worry.

Her waspish-headed son has broke his arrows,
Swears he will shoot no more but play with sparrows
And be a boy right out.

CERES

        Highest queen of state,
Great Juno, comes; I know her by her gait.

Enter JUNO

JUNO

How does my bounteous sister? Go with me
To bless this twain, that they may prosperous be
And honored in their issue.

They sing:

JUNO

Honor, riches, marriage blessing,
Long continuance, and increasing,
Hourly joys be still upon you!
Juno sings her blessings on you.

CERES

Earth's increase, foison plenty,
Barns and garners never empty,
Vines and clust'ring bunches growing,
Plants with goodly burden bowing;
Spring come to you at the farthest
In the very end of harvest!
Scarcity and want shall shun you;
Ceres' blessing so is on you.

FERDINAND

This is a most majestic vision, and
Harmoniously charmingly. May I be bold
To think these spirits?

PROSPERO

        Spirits, which by mine art
I have from their confines called to enact
My present fancies.

FERDINAND

        Let me live here ever;
So rare a wond'red father and a wise
Makes this place Paradise.

Juno and Ceres whisper, and send Iris on employment

PROSPERO

        Sweet, now, silence!
Juno and Ceres whisper seriously;
There's something else to do: hush, and be mute,
Or else our spell is marred.

IRIS

You nymphs, call naiads, of the windring brooks,
With your sedged crowns and ever-harmless looks,
Leave your crisp channels and on this green land
Answer your summons; Juno does command:

64 ACT IV SCENE 1

Translation: Venus and her son tried to get Ferdinand and Miranda to break their "no hanky-panky" vow, but they failed. Now, her son Cupid has resigned as love's arrow shooter. So they won't be at the party.

issue = children

foison = abundant harvest

garners = granaries

Notice all the agricultural references in Ceres' blessing. This goddess has a one-track mind!

Modest, aren't we, Prospero?

In marrying Miranda, Ferdy gets a master magician for a father.

windring = mix of "winding" and "wandering"

Come, temperate nymphs, and help to celebrate
A contract of true love; be not too late.

Enter certain Nymphs

Nymphs are female spirits.

You sunburnt sicklemen, of August weary,
Come hither from the furrow and be merry:
Make holiday; your rye-straw hats put on
And these fresh nymphs encounter every one
In country footing.

sicklemen = mowers (as in grass)
A furrow is a groove made by a plow.

Looks like Juno is calling all her friends—no one's going to miss this celebration!

Enter certain Reapers, properly habited: they join with the Nymphs in a graceful dance; towards the end whereof PROSPERO starts suddenly, and speaks; after which, to a strange, hollow, and confused noise, they heavily vanish

Goddesses, nymphs, reapers, spirits: This is turning out to be some party—until Prospero rains on everyone's parade.

PROSPERO

[Aside] I had forgot that foul conspiracy
Of the beast Caliban and his confederates
Against my life: the minute of their plot
Is almost come.

No wonder he's a party-pooper. He has to keep himself from getting murdered!

To the Spirits

Well done! avoid; no more!

FERDINAND

This is strange: your father's in some passion
That works him strongly.

MIRANDA

Never till this day
Saw I him touched with anger so distempered.

So Ferdy and Miranda haven't heard about Caliban's plot with the clowns to take over the island.

PROSPERO

You do look, my son, in a moved sort,
As if you were dismayed: be cheerful, sir.
Our revels now are ended. These our actors,
As I foretold you, were all spirits and
Are melted into air, into thin air:
And, like the baseless fabric of this vision,
The cloud-capped towers, the gorgeous palaces,
The solemn temples, the great globe itself,
Yea all which it inherit, shall dissolve
And, like this insubstantial pageant faded,
Leave not a rack behind. We are such stuff
As dreams are made on, and our little life
Is rounded with a sleep. Sir, I am vexed;
Bear with my weakness; my old brain is troubled:
Be not disturbed with my infirmity:
If you be pleased, retire into my cell
And there repose: a turn or two I'll walk,
To still my beating mind.

moved sort = troubled

One of Shakespeare's most famous speeches. "Revels" is another word for "entertainments."

baseless fabric = ethereal substance

DOUBLE MEANING ALERT!! The "great globe" can refer to the world or to Shakespeare's Globe Theatre in London.

A rack is a wisp of a cloud.

Like these spirits, our lives are fleeting.

"Sir": Prospero now speaks to Ferdinand.

FERDINAND, MIRANDA

We wish your peace.

Exeunt

PROSPERO

Come with a thought I thank thee, Ariel: come.

Enter ARIEL

ARIEL

Thy thoughts I cleave to. What's thy pleasure?

PROSPERO

Spirit,
We must prepare to meet with Caliban.

ARIEL

Ay, my commander: when I presented Ceres,
I thought to have told thee of it, but I feared
Lest I might anger thee.

PROSPERO

Say again, where didst thou leave these varlets?

ARIEL

I told you, sir, they were red-hot with drinking;
So fun of valor that they smote the air
For breathing in their faces; beat the ground
For kissing of their feet; yet always bending
Towards their project. Then I beat my tabor;
At which, like unbacked colts, they pricked
their ears,
Advanced their eyelids, lifted up their noses
As they smelt music: so I charmed their ears
That calf-like they my lowing followed through
Toothed briers, sharp furzes, pricking goss and thorns,
Which entered their frail shins: at last I left them
I' th' filthy mantled pool beyond your cell,
There dancing up to th' chins, that the foul lake
O'erstunk their feet.

PROSPERO

This was well done, my bird.
Thy shape invisible retain thou still:
The trumpery in my house, go bring it hither,
For stale to catch these thieves.

ARIEL

I go, I go.

Exit

PROSPERO

A devil, a born devil, on whose nature
Nurture can never stick; on whom my pains,
Humanely taken, all, all lost, quite lost;
And as with age his body uglier grows,
So his mind cankers. I will plague them all,
Even to roaring.

Re-enter ARIEL, loaden with glistering apparel, &c

Come, hang them on this line.

**PROSPERO and ARIEL remain invisible. Enter CALIBAN,
STEPHANO, and TRINCULO, all wet**

---

cleave = cling

Note to Ariel: The right time to
tell someone about a plan to kill
them is immediately!!

varlets = rascals

Sounds like Caliban and his
cronies aren't in much of a
condition to do anything!

unbacked colts = untrained
horses

Ariel compares Stephano,
Trinculo, and Caliban to a bunch
of cows, first caught in the
briars, then trapped in a
scummy pool.

trumpery = worthless bric-a-brac

stale = decoy

Prospero finally comes down
squarely on the "nature vs.
nurture" debate. The truth hurts:
he nurtured Caliban like his own
son.

glistering = an old-fashioned
word for glistening

CALIBAN

    Pray you, tread softly, that the blind mole may not
    Hear a foot fall: we now are near his cell.

Moles, unable to see well, are said to have an extra-developed sense of hearing.

STEPHANO

    Monster, your fairy, which you say is
    a harmless fairy, has done little better than
    played the Jack with us.

Jack = knave

TRINCULO

    Monster, I do smell all horse-piss; at
    which my nose is in great indignation.

STEPHANO

    So is mine. Do you hear, monster? If I should take
    a displeasure against you, look you,—

TRINCULO

    Thou wert but a lost monster.

CALIBAN

    Good my lord, give me thy favor still.
    Be patient, for the prize I'll bring thee to
    Shall hoodwink this mischance: therefore speak softly.
    All's hushed as midnight yet.

Translation: What's coming to you will make smelling like a sewer worth it!

TRINCULO

    Ay, but to lose our bottles in the pool,—

STEPHANO

    There is not only disgrace and dishonor in that,
    monster, but an infinite loss.

TRINCULO

    That's more to me than my wetting: yet this is your
    harmless fairy, monster.

STEPHANO

    I will fetch off my bottle, though I be o'er ears
    for my labor.

Looks like it's time to stop drinking wine, unless someone wants to do some deep-scum diving.

CALIBAN

    Prithee, my king, be quiet. Seest thou here,
    This is the mouth o' th' cell: no noise, and enter.
    Do that good mischief which may make this island
    Thine own for ever, and I, thy Caliban,
    For aye thy foot- licker.

Can mischief be good? Notice how Shakespeare puts opposite ideas together.

STEPHANO

    Give me thy hand. I do begin to have bloody thoughts.

TRINCULO

    O King Stephano! O peer! O worthy Stephano! look
    what a wardrobe here is for thee!

First the music, now the clothes— these "killers" are easily distracted!

CALIBAN

    Let it alone, thou fool; it is but trash.

TRINCULO

    O, ho, monster! we know what belongs to a frippery.
    O King Stephano!

frippery = used-clothing store

STEPHANO

Put off that gown, Trinculo; by this hand, I'll have
that gown.

TRINCULO

Thy grace shall have it.

Thy grace, King Stephano—
these guys get off on pretending
they're royalty.

CALIBAN

The dropsy drown this fool! What do you mean
To dote thus on such luggage? Let's alone
And do the murder first: if he awake,
From toe to crown he'll fill our skins with pinches,
Make us strange stuff.

Dropsy is a disease where
water collects in the body—
sounds pretty awful!

Luggage means junk: Caliban
knows these clowns need to
move fast to get the better of
Prospero!

STEPHANO

Be you quiet, monster. Mistress line,
is not this my jerkin? Now is the jerkin under
the line: now, jerkin, you are like to lose your
hair and prove a bald jerkin.

What's with all the "jerkin"
jokes? A jerkin is a short coat;
"line" refers to both a clothesline
and to the equator, where
people were thought to catch
fevers and lose their hair. Still
not getting it? The jokes are
pretty out of date.

TRINCULO

Do, do: we steal by line and level, an't like your Grace.

by line and level = by the rules

STEPHANO

I thank thee for that jest; here's a garment for't:
wit shall not go unrewarded while I am king of this
country. 'Steal by line and level' is an excellent
pass of pate; there's another garment for't.

excellent pass of pate = clever
turn of phrase

TRINCULO

Monster, come, put some lime upon your fingers, and
away with the rest.

Lime, as in bird-lime, was this
sticky stuff used to catch birds.

CALIBAN

I will have none on't: we shall lose our time,
And all be turned to barnacles, or to apes
With foreheads villainous low.

Barnacles (shellfish) or apes?!
Caliban knows what Prospero
might do if he catches these
jokers.

STEPHANO

Monster, lay-to your fingers: help to bear this
away where my hogshead of wine is, or I'll turn you
out of my kingdom: go to, carry this.

TRINCULO

And this.

Stop loading Caliban up with
clothes, dudes! Can't you see
where this is leading?

STEPHANO

Ay, and this.

*A noise of hunters heard. Enter divers Spirits, in shape of
dogs and hounds, and hunt them about, PROSPERO and
ARIEL setting them on*

Evidently not. And they've really
let the dogs out this time.

PROSPERO

Hey, Mountain, hey!

Mountain, Fury, Silver, and
Tyrant are the names of
Prospero's invisible dogs.

ARIEL

Silver I there it goes, Silver!

PROSPERO

Fury, Fury! there, Tyrant, there! hark! hark!

CALIBAN, STEPHANO, and TRINCULO, are driven out

>Go charge my goblins that they grind their joints
>With dry convulsions, shorten up their sinews
>With aged cramps, and more pinch-spotted make them
>Than pard or cat o' mountain.

ARIEL

>Hark, they roar!

PROSPERO

>Let them be hunted soundly. At this hour
>Lie at my mercy all mine enemies:
>Shortly shall all my labors end, and thou
>Shalt have the air at freedom: for a little
>Follow, and do me service.

Exeunt

Ouch! Prospero's Rule #5: Do unto others BEFORE they do unto you.

Translation: Give them more red spots from pinching than a leopard has.

The master plan is coming together—Prospero has everyone where he wants them!

Act IV Notes

Act IV Notes

Act IV Notes

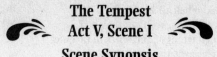

The Tempest
Act V, Scene I
Scene Synopsis

Success at last for Prospero! Everyone is getting just what they deserve—or are they? His super-spells are so strong that even Ariel, who lacks human emotions, feels sorry for his enemies. Prospero reworks his master plan of revenge to include forgiveness and sets everyone free from their torture. King Alonso restores Prospero's dukedom (sorry, Antonio!), and Prospero reveals Ferdinand and his new squeeze Miranda to King Alonso. Prospero vows to give up the magic that has kept him isolated from others and rejoins the rest of the world.

Scene I

Before PROSPERO'S cell.

Enter PROSPERO in his magic robes, and ARIEL

PROSPERO

Now does my project gather to a head:
My charms crack not; my spirits obey; and time
Goes upright with his carriage. How's the day?

> H.E.T. Moment: Personification of time, who can stand up straight because his load is light.

ARIEL

On the sixth hour; at which time, my lord,
You said our work should cease.

PROSPERO

    I did say so,
When first I raised the tempest. Say, my spirit,
How fares the King and 's followers?

ARIEL

    Confined together
In the same fashion as you gave in charge,
Just as you left them; all prisoners, sir,
In the line grove which weather-fends your cell
They cannot budge till your release. The King,
His brother and yours, abide all three distracted
And the remainder mourning over them,
Brimful of sorrow and dismay; but chiefly
Him that you termed, sir, 'The good old Lord Gonzalo;'
His tears run down his beard, like winter's drops
From eaves of reeds. Your charm so strongly works 'em
That if you now beheld them, your affections
Would become tender.

> Ah, the power! King Alonso and his gang are still in fits, trapped in a lime-tree orchard until Prospero says they can leave.

> eaves of reeds = a roof made of thatch

> Wow! Prospero's revenge must have put Alonso and the gang at rock bottom if spirit can feel sorry for them.

PROSPERO

    Dost thou think so, spirit?

ARIEL

Mine would, sir, were I human.

PROSPERO

    And mine shall.
Hast thou, which art but air, a touch, a feeling
Of their afflictions, and shall not myself,

> Looks like our master magician is rethinking his master plan.

One of their kind, that relish all as sharply,
Passion as they, be kindlier moved than thou art?
Though with their high wrongs I am struck to th' quick,
Yet with my nobler reason 'gainst my fury
Do I take part: the rarer action is
In virtue than in vengeance: they being penitent,
The sole drift of my purpose doth extend
Not a frown further. Go release them, Ariel:
My charms I'll break, their senses I'll restore,
And they shall be themselves.

ARIEL
       I'll fetch them, sir.

Exit

PROSPERO
Ye elves of hills, brooks, standing lakes and groves,
And ye that on the sands with printless foot
Do chase the ebbing Neptune and do fly him
When he comes back; you demi-puppets that
By moonshine do the green sour ringlets make,
Whereof the ewe not bites, and you whose pastime
Is to make midnight mushrooms, that rejoice
To hear the solemn curfew; by whose aid,
Weak masters though ye be, I have bedimmed
The noontide sun, called forth the mutinous winds,
And 'twixt the green sea and the azured vault
Set roaring war: to the dread rattling thunder
Have I given fire and rifted Jove's stout oak
With his own bolt; the strong-based promontory
Have I made shake and by the spurs plucked up
The pine and cedar: graves at my command
Have waked their sleepers, oped, and let 'em forth
By my so potent art. But this rough magic
I here abjure, and, when I have required
Some heavenly music, which even now I do,
To work mine end upon their senses that
This airy charm is for, I'll break my staff,
Bury it certain fathoms in the earth,
And deeper than did ever plummet sound
I'll drown my book.

Solemn music

*Re-enter ARIEL before: then ALONSO, with a frantic gesture,
attended by GONZALO; SEBASTIAN and ANTONIO in like
manner, attended by ADRIAN and FRANCISCO they all enter
the circle which PROSPERO had made, and there stand
charmed; which PROSPERO observing, speaks:*

A solemn air and the best comforter
To an unsettled fancy cure thy brains,
Now useless, boil'd within thy skull! There stand,
For you are spell-stopped.
Holy Gonzalo, honorable man,

That's right, Prospero, Alonso and the others are only human, just like you.

Major Moral Moment: Prospero chooses mercy over revenge.

Another famous speech—Prospero describes his magical powers and then promises to give them up.

demi-puppets = doll-like fairy creatures

Green sour ringlets are fairy circles in the grass.

azured vault = blue sky

Those are some major magical powers! Lightning, earthquakes, even raising the dead, all at Prospero's command!

abjure = renounce upon oath

DOUBLE MEANING ALERT!! Prospero's willing to give up his powers to rejoin humanity; Shakespeare is said to have retired after writing *The Tempest*. Could this be the Bard's final goodbye?

"Air" here means song, which is the best comforter to anxiety.

Mine eyes, ev'n sociable to the show of thine,
Fall fellowly drops. The charm dissolves apace,
And as the morning steals upon the night,
Melting the darkness, so their rising senses
Begin to chase the ignorant fumes that mantle
Their clearer reason. O good Gonzalo,
My true preserver, and a loyal Sir
To him you follow'st! I will pay thy graces
Home both in word and deed. Most cruelly
Didst thou, Alonso, use me and my daughter:
Thy brother was a furtherer in the act.
Thou art pinched for't now, Sebastian. Flesh and blood,
You, brother mine, that entertained ambition,
Expelled remorse and nature; who, with Sebastian,
Whose inward pinches therefore are most strong,
Would here have killed your king; I do forgive thee,
Unnatural though thou art. Their understanding
Begins to swell, and the approaching tide
Will shortly fill the reasonable shore
That now lies foul and muddy. Not one of them
That yet looks on me, or would know me Ariel,
Fetch me the hat and rapier in my cell:
I will discase me, and myself present
As I was sometime Milan: quickly, spirit;
Thou shalt ere long be free.

ARIEL *sings and helps to attire him*

Where the bee sucks. there suck I:
In a cowslip's bell I lie;
There I couch when owls do cry.
On the bat's back I do fly
After summer merrily.
Merrily, merrily shall I live now
Under the blossom that hangs on the bough.

PROSPERO

Why, that's my dainty Ariel! I shall miss thee:
But yet thou shalt have freedom: so, so, so.
To the King's ship, invisible as thou art:
There shalt thou find the mariners asleep
Under the hatches; the master and the boatswain
Being awake, enforce them to this place,
And presently, I prithee.
Ariel. I drink the air before me, and return
Or ere your pulse twice beat.

Exit

GONZALO

All torment, trouble, wonder and amazement
Inhabits here: some heavenly power guide us
Out of this fearful country!

---

sociable to the show = sympathetic to the sight of Gonzalo's tears

H.E.T. Moment: Note the simile comparing the charm's disappearance to the dawning of the day. (mantle = hide)

Translation: I'll tell everyone this straight-up dude rocks!

furtherer = helper

remorse and nature = guilt and natural responses

Nature vs. nurture again: Antonio had a nobleman's advantages but he still dissed his own bro— nature or learned behavior?

Another sea reference! Ocean as reason.

After twelve years on the island, Prospero isn't exactly a fashion plate. He'll jog everybody's memory with his old hat.

"discase"—i.e., lose the magic robe

cowslip = primrose

So the mariners got to snooze through the whole play . . .

presently = immediately

. . . unlike Gonzalo, who has been in a living nightmare!

PROSPERO

    Behold, sir King,
The wronged Duke of Milan, Prospero:
For more assurance that a living prince
Does now speak to thee, I embrace thy body;
And to thee and thy company I bid
A hearty welcome.

Looks like the real Duke of Milan
is finally standing up!

ALONSO

    Whe'r thou be'st he or no,
Or some enchanted trifle to abuse me,
As late I have been, I not know: thy pulse
Beats as of flesh and blood; and, since I saw thee,
The affliction of my mind amends, with which,
I fear, a madness held me: this must crave,
An if this be at all, a most strange story.
Thy dukedom I resign and do entreat
Thou pardon me my wrongs. But how should Prospero
Be living and be here?

Whe'r = a squished together
"whether"

After all this hocus-pocus, it's hard
to believe that Prospero's for real!

crave = require

An if this be at all = if I believe my
eyes

Now that Prospero's back, no more
payments to Naples! (That was
easy.)

PROSPERO

    First, noble friend,
Let me embrace thine age, whose honor cannot
Be measured or confined.

Prospero speaks to Gonzalo here.

GONZALO

    Whether this be
Or be not, I'll not swear.

PROSPERO

    You do yet taste
Some subtleties o' th' isle, that will not let you
Believe things certain. Welcome, my friends all!

Subtleties o' th' isle? Hello!?
They've been in pretty UN-subtle
fits for the past hour. No wonder
they doubt he's real.

Aside to SEBASTIAN and ANTONIO

But you, my brace of lords, were I so minded,
I here could pluck his Highness' frown upon you
And justify you traitors: at this time
I will tell no tales.

Brace yourselves, you brace (pair)
of posers; Prospero's got the dirt
on you!

SEBASTIAN

    [Aside] The devil speaks in him.

PROSPERO

    No.
For you, most wicked sir, whom to call brother
Would even infect my mouth, I do forgive
Thy rankest fault; all of them; and require
My dukedom of thee, which perforce, I know,
Thou must restore.

rankest = most disgusting

Nice of you to ask, Prospero, since
he has to say yes anyway.

ALONSO

    If thou beest Prospero,
Give us particulars of thy preservation;
How thou hast met us here, who three hours since
Were wracked upon this shore; where I have lost–
How sharp the point of this remembrance is!–
My dear son Ferdinand.

Where is automatic replay when
you need it? Prospero told Miranda
the whole "preservation" story in
Act I, Scene II!

PROSPERO

    I am woe for't, sir.

ALONSO

    Irreparable is the loss, and patience
    Says it is past her cure.

PROSPERO

    I rather think
    You have not sought her help, of whose soft grace
    For the like loss I have her sovereign aid
    And rest myself content.

ALONSO

    You the like loss!

PROSPERO

    As great to me, as late; and, supportable
    To make the dear loss, have I means much weaker
    Than you may call to comfort you, for I
    Have lost my daughter.

ALONSO

    A daughter?
    O heavens, that they were living both in Naples,
    The King and Queen there! that they were, I wish
    Myself were mudded in the oozy bed
    Where my son lies. When did you lose your daughter?

PROSPERO

    In this last tempest. I perceive these lords
    At this encounter do so much admire
    That they devour their reason and scarce think
    Their eyes do offices of truth, their words
    Are natural breath: but, howsoev'r you have
    Been justled from your senses, know for certain
    That I am Prospero and that very duke
    Which was thrust forth of Milan, who most strangely
    Upon this shore, where you were wracked, was landed,
    To be the lord on't. No more yet of this;
    For 'tis a chronicle of day by day,
    Not a relation for a breakfast nor
    Befitting this first meeting. Welcome, sir;
    This cell's my court: here have I few attendants
    And subjects none abroad: pray you, look in.
    My dukedom since you have given me again,
    I will requite you with as good a thing;
    At least bring forth a wonder, to content ye
    As much as me my dukedom.

Here PROSPERO discovers FERDINAND and MIRANDA playing at chess

MIRANDA

    Sweet lord, you play me false.

FERDINAND
　　No, my dearest love,
I would not for the world.

MIRANDA
　　Yes, for a score of kingdoms you should wrangle,
And I would call it, fair play.

ALONSO
　　If this prove
A vision of the island, one dear son
Shall I twice lose.

Still doubting his own eyes—
Prospero's antics have lasting
effects!

SEBASTIAN
　　A most high miracle!

FERDINAND
　　Though the seas threaten, they are merciful;
I have cursed them without cause.

Ferdinand is seeing his
supposedly-dead father alive
again for the first time.

Kneels

ALONSO
　　Now all the blessings
Of a glad father compass thee about!
Arise, and say how thou cam'st here.

compass = encompass

MIRANDA
　　O, wonder!
How many goodly creatures are there here!
How beauteous mankind is! O brave new world,
That has such people in't!

After twelve years on the island
seeing only two other people,
seven more seem like a crowd!

PROSPERO
　　'Tis new to thee.

ALONSO
　　What is this maid with whom thou wast at play?
Your eld'st acquaintance cannot be three hours:
Is she the goddess that hath severed us,
And brought us thus together?

Shakespeare Reminder: all this
stuff happens in only three hours.
Uh, not exactly. Your son's been
busy.

FERDINAND
　　Sir, she is mortal;
But by immortal providence she's mine:
I chose her when I could not ask my father
For his advice, nor thought I had one. She
Is daughter to this famous Duke of Milan,
Of whom so often I have heard renown,
But never saw before; of whom I have
Received a second life; and second father
This lady makes him to me.

Providence: again, a reference to
fate.

of = from

ALONSO
　　I am hers:
But, O, how oddly will it sound that I
Must ask my child forgiveness!

her second father, that is

PROSPERO
　　There, sir, stop:

Let us not burden our remembrance with
A heaviness that's gone.

GONZALO

> I have inly wept,
> Or should have spoke ere this. Look down, you gods,
> And on this couple drop a blessed crown!
> For it is you that have chalked forth the way
> Which brought us hither.

ALONSO

> I say, Amen, Gonzalo!

GONZALO

> Was Milan thrust from Milan, that his issue
> Should become kings of Naples? O, rejoice
> Beyond a common joy, and set it down
> With gold on lasting pillars: In one voyage
> Did Claribel her husband find at Tunis,
> And Ferdinand, her brother, found a wife
> Where he himself was lost, Prospero his dukedom
> In a poor isle and all of us ourselves
> When no man was his own.

ALONSO

> *[To FERDINAND and MIRANDA]* Give me your hands:
> Let grief and sorrow still embrace his heart
> That doth not wish you joy!

GONZALO

> Be it so! Amen!

Re-enter ARIEL, with the Master and Boatswain amazedly following

> O, look, sir, look, sir! here is more of us:
> I prophesied, if a gallows were on land,
> This fellow could not drown. Now, blasphemy,
> That swear'st grace o'erboard, not an oath on shore?
> Hast thou no mouth by land? What is the news?

Boatswain

> The best news is, that we have safely found
> Our king and company; the next, our ship–
> Which, but three glasses since, we gave out split–
> Is tight and yare and bravely rigged as when
> We first put out to sea.

ARIEL

> *[Aside to PROSPERO]* Sir, all this service
> Have I done since I went.

PROSPERO

> *[Aside to ARIEL]* My tricksy spirit!

ALONSO

> These are not natural events; they strengthen
> From strange to stranger. Say, how came you hither?

DOUBLE MEANING ALERT!!
Alonso's grief over Ferdy is gone,
but Prospero's anger toward his
brother is also lessened.

So was all of this, starting with
Prospero's banishment, just a
spoke on the Wheel of Fortune?

Gonzalo was right: The Bo-zen IS
going to die by hanging, not
drowning! (Eeuw—what a thing
to look forward to!)

Translation: You drive goodness
from the ship with cursing, but
don't swear on land.

gave out = reported to be
yare = in good condition

tricksy = clever

Boatswain

    If I did think, sir, I were well awake,
    I'd strive to tell you. We are dead of sleep,
    And–how we know not–all clapped under hatches;   *held under the deck*
    Where but even now with strange and several noises   *Next time we need good sound*
    Of roaring, shrieking, howling, jingling chains,   *effects, we know whom to ask!*
    And moe diversity of sounds, all horrible,   *moe = more*
    We were awaked; straightway, at liberty;
    Where we, in all her trim, freshly beheld   *in all her trim = in our styling*
    Our royal, good and gallant ship, our master   *clothes*
    Cap'ring to eye her: on a trice, so please you,
    Even in a dream, were we divided from them   *Cap'ring = doing a dance*
    And were brought moping hither.   *Translation: Instantly we were*
    brought here in a trance.

ARIEL

    [Aside to PROSPERO] Was't well done?

PROSPERO

    [Aside to ARIEL] Bravely, my diligence. Thou shalt be free.

ALONSO

    This is as strange a maze as e'er men trod   *That's right, Alonso. Prospero's*
    And there is in this business more than nature   *power OVER nature had a lot to*
    Was ever conduct of: some oracle   *do with it.*
    Must rectify our knowledge.

PROSPERO

        Sir, my liege,
    Do not infest your mind with beating on   *Translation: Fuh-get about it!*
    The strangeness of this business; at picked leisure
    Which shall be shortly, single I'll resolve you,   *i.e., tell you later*
    Which to you shall seem probable, of every
    These happened accidents; till when, be cheerful
    And think of each thing well.

Aside to ARIEL

    Come hither, spirit:
    Set Caliban and his companions free;
    Untie the spell.

Exit ARIEL

    How fares my gracious sir?
    There are yet missing of your company
    Some few odd lads that you remember not.

Re-enter ARIEL, driving in CALIBAN, STEPHANO and
TRINCULO, in their stolen apparel

STEPHANO

    Every man shift for all the rest, and   *shift = practice, devise*
    let no man take care of himself; for all is
    but fortune. Coragio, bully-monster, coragio!   *coragio = courage*

TRINCULO

    If these be true spies which I wear in my head,   *Trinculo says this upon seeing*
    here's a goodly sight.   *Prospero, Alonso, and the rest of*
    the gang.

CALIBAN

O Setebos, these be brave spirits indeed!
How fine my master is! I am afraid
He will chastise me.

SEBASTIAN

Ha, ha!
What things are these, my Lord Antonio?
Will money buy 'em?

ANTONIO

Very like; one of them
Is a plain fish, and, no doubt, marketable.

PROSPERO

Mark but the badges of these men, my lords,
Then say if they be true. This misshapen knave,
His mother was a witch, and one so strong
That could control the moon, make flows and ebbs,
And deal in her command without her power.
These three have robbed me; and this demi-devil–
For he's a bastard one–had plotted with them
To take my life. Two of these fellows you
Must know and own; this thing of darkness!
Acknowledge mine.

CALIBAN

I shall be pinched to death.

ALONSO

Is not this Stephano, my drunken butler?

SEBASTIAN

He is drunk now: where had he wine?

ALONSO

And Trinculo is reeling ripe: where should they
Find this grand liquor that hath gilded 'em
How camest thou in this pickle?

TRINCULO

I have been in such a pickle since I
saw you last that, I fear me, will never out of
my bones: I shall not fear fly-blowing.

SEBASTIAN

Why, how now, Stephano!

STEPHANO

O, touch me not; I am not Stephano, but a cramp.

PROSPERO

You'ld be king o' the isle, sirrah?

STEPHANO

I should have been a sore one then.

ALONSO

This is a strange thing as e'er I looked on.

Pointing to Caliban

Remember, Caliban isn't exactly an expert on humanity: up till now, he's only met four people, and two of them are drunks.

What is with these people?! Everyone who meets Caliban wants to sell him!

badges = garments

DOUBLE MEANING ALERT!!
Prospero claims Caliban—and all his baser traits—as his own. The low and the lofty: both are inside Prospero. He can choose which "nature" to pursue.

reeling ripe = drunk as a skunk

"Sore" as in pathetic and "sore" as in hurting (from Prospero's charms).

PROSPERO

He is as disproportioned in his manners
As in his shape. Go, sirrah, to my cell;
Take with you your companions; as you look
To have my pardon, trim it handsomely.

disproportioned = disfigured

Prospero speaks to Caliban here.

"Sirrah" is how you address an underling.

trim it handsomely = fix the place up

CALIBAN

Ay, that I will; and I'll be wise hereafter
And seek for grace. What a thrice-double ass
Was I, to take this drunkard for a god
And worship this dull fool!

Well, Caliban, hindsight is always 20/20!

PROSPERO

Go to; away!

ALONSO

Hence, and bestow your luggage where you found it.

SEBASTIAN

Or stole it, rather.

Exeunt CALIBAN, STEPHANO, and TRINCULO

PROSPERO

Sir, I invite your Highness and your train
To my poor cell, where you shall take your rest
For this one night; which, part of it, I'll waste
With such discourse as, I not doubt, shall make it
Go quick away; the story of my life
And the particular accidents gone by
Since I came to this isle: and in the morn
I'll bring you to your ship and so to Naples,
Where I have hope to see the nuptial
Of these our dear-beloved solemnized;
And thence retire me to my Milan, where
Every third thought shall be my grave.

train = royal entourage

waste = spend, while away

Which leads us to wonder what the first and second thoughts will be. Any guesses?

ALONSO

I long
To hear the story of your life, which must
Take the ear strangely.

PROSPERO

I'll deliver all;
And promise you calm seas, auspicious gales
And sail so expeditious that shall catch
Your royal fleet far off.

Don't worry, Alonso; he'll give you the dirt.

expeditious = speedy

Aside to ARIEL

My Ariel, chick,
That is thy charge: then to the elements
Be free, and fare thou well! Please you, draw near.

FINALLY, Ariel is free—but not until he casts one last "calm-sea" spell.

"Please you, draw near" is often addressed to the audience.

Exeunt

EPILOGUE
SPOKEN BY PROSPERO

Now my charms are all o'erthrown,
And what strength I have's mine own,
Which is most faint: now, 'tis true,
I must be here confined by you,
Or sent to Naples. Let me not,
Since I have my dukedom got
And pardoned the deceiver, dwell
In this bare island by your spell;
But release me from my bands
With the help of your good hands:
Gentle breath of yours my sails
Must fill, or else my project fails,
Which was to please. Now I want
Spirits to enforce, art to enchant,
And my ending is despair,
Unless I be relieved by prayer,
Which pierces so that it assaults
Mercy itself and frees all faults
As you from crimes would pardoned be,
Let your indulgence set me free.

Exit

The island image again: Prospero gives up his magic and elects to leave his isolation, instead reaching out to his fellow humans—and the audience. The man's not a wizard anymore, but he's also not an island.

Prospero asks us to accept him and free him from his isolation.

CONGRATULATIONS! You've just "indulged" in *The Tempest*! Rock on!

Act V Notes

Act V Notes

Act V Notes

Fun Globe Facts

1 The Heavens at the New Globe weigh 16 tons. To find oak trees suitable for their support involved a six–month search before one was found in the borders of Scotland and the other in Norfolk.

2 The recent rebuilding of Shakespeare's Globe Theatre has resulted in a few never–before–considered hazards of acting during Shakespeare's time. The floor of the stage was originally thought to be made of hazelwood, but as modern actors began walking and moving about, the new surface produced a fine dust — choking many of the actors and making Shakespeare's language nearly unspeakable!

3 Small piggybank–like boxes were placed near the entranceways of theatres for attending patrons to place their money. These boxes were then gathered and placed in a room under lock–and–key; from this, we derive our modern-day term of "box office."

4 Did you know that St. Iago drove the Moors out of Spain, so an Elizabethan audience would've expected Iago to be the good guy?
Othello was the first Moor not to be a villain!

5 Lord Alderman and his men HATED theatrical audiences and believed only the scum of the earth gathered there: "theeves (sic), horse-stealers, whoremongers, cozeners, cony–catching persons, practicers of treason, and such other like."

6 The Globe (in Will's time) could accommodate as many as 3,000 heads . . . 1,000 of which were usually groundlings!

7 Boxes nearest the stage in the lowermost story were the "Lord's Rooms" (labeled "orchestra" in de Witt's sketch): admission was 12 pence. Ben Jonson refers to the "six-penny mechanicks" who busied themselves with whores in the darkened corners of the boxes. Food and drink in unlimited amounts were included in the admission price if a comedy was playing. Especially when you consider that the audience was packed in like sardines (3,000 heads), it's not surprising that, if people were drinking ale, they would grow so drunk that they'd pee on others—either because they didn't feel like walking to a rest area or just for fun. Now that's entertainment!

8 Elizabethan theatre developed as perhaps the first form of sensational mass entertainment, showing all its action to the audience via the third-person perspective. The appeal is akin to the modern medium of TV.

9 *Macbeth*, *The Winter's Tale*, and *Cymbeline* all performed in 1611 at the Globe.

10 *Macbeth* performed at the Globe in the afternoon (in daylight) court for James I and the King of Denmark, and indoors at Blackfriar's.

11 Simon Forman's eyewitness account of a performance in 1611 describes one of the most frightening scenes: "The ghost of Banquo came and sat beside him. And Macbeth turning about to sit down again saw the ghost which fronted him so that he fell in a great passion of fear. . . ."

12 Macbeth has been portrayed as a WWI survivor, Adolf Hitler, and a present-day fascist.